FIGURES OF SPEECH

FIGURES OF SPEECH

by

Phyllida Garth

Illustrated by

Felix Potter

Tabb House

First published 1990
Tabb House Ltd, 7 Church Street, Padstow, Cornwall, PL28 8BG

ISBN 0 907018 70 X

Typeset by St George Typesetting, Redruth, Cornwall
Printed and bound by Bookcraft Ltd, Midsomer Norton

THE girls' private schools I describe really existed in the 1930s, though they were not called by the names I have given them and I have not indicated their locations except to say that they were all fairly near London, in various directions.

The characters are real people but, again, they bear other names and one or two are an amalgam of several individuals.

The Evening Classes and the Church Drama Group are exact, though names are fictitious.

Ph.G.

LIST OF ILLUSTRATIONS

CONTENTS

PART I

PART II

PART III

PART I

Autumn and Winter, 1938

BAYSWATER

THIS is the second week of the autumn term. The September sun pours through the window onto my writing-table. It's Sunday morning so I'm at home and the mews is quiet, with only the Daimler which lives under my flat, and one or two purring, chauffeur-driven cars being taken out, presumably to convey their rich and elderly owners to church or to visit friends. Until a few months ago I could hear horses shifting and blowing below me. I liked that. It made me feel there was still something of the country left, even here in Bayswater. But then the stables were converted into a garage (as they had been long ago in the rest of the mews) and the horses were taken away. Now there are just these great, sleek cars and their smart chauffeurs who, when they are hatless and in shirt-sleeves, shout to each other and whistle as they clean their precious monsters, call out jovial remarks to me when I come out of my front door, but become very dignified and proper once they are in uniform, and barely pass the time of day.

Mine is the only flat this side of the mews, but opposite me is another one occupied by Helen Strickland, a writer of magazine stories. Both our flats must at one time have been hay-lofts for each has a stable door on the landing, of which the bottom half has been boarded up though we

. . . call out jovial remarks to me

can still open the top half and talk to each other across the narrow end of the mews. We occasionally visit each other for coffee but only when invited; we don't just drop in. This has been the unspoken rule ever since I took this flat two years ago and it suits us both equally for we are busy people and anyway have our own friends.

Helen is in her thirties, a good ten years older than me, and she is lucky to work at home while I, a visiting teacher, have to travel every day in a different direction to various girls' private schools in the Home Counties. Some days I spend longer in travelling than in teaching and I have an intimate acquaintance with several of London's main-line stations. When, at our first meeting, I told Helen I taught Speech and Drama, she at once said, "Oh, you mean El-o-cu-tion. 'How now brown cow,' and that sort of thing?" I get awfully bored with this well-worn and faintly mocking joke, but I managed a wan smile and a brief explanation of what my job entailed. People's eyes glaze over if one holds forth for too long.

Two private pupils come here on Saturday mornings. One is an Elementary schoolteacher seeking guidance as to what to teach a class of rampageous young children in a poor district of Marylebone and how best to improve her reading aloud of stories and poems. I was faced with just such a class on teaching-practice during my training and, in spite of help from a kind and watchful headmistress, I think I was a disaster. I've learnt a bit since then and hope the ideas I dish out to this conscientious girl may help her, for she is intelligent and imaginative, seizes on whatever she thinks may be of use to her and ignores the rest.

My second pupil is a harmless, acquiescent girl with an ambitious mother and a pretty face. She is possessed of neither intelligence nor imagination but is constantly made to recite at parties and verse-speaking competitions. Her mother likes to tell me of all the compliments

3

received after each of these occasions. I would happily do without this poor girl but I need the money.

Occasionally, during the holidays, Rupert comes along. He is a sixteen-year-old Etonian, the son of friends of my Uncle Charles who lives in the same opulent block of flats as they do, in Belgravia. It seems to be fashionable for public-school boys to talk without moving their lips or using their voices (I have met one from Shrewsbury and another from Westminster) and I think perhaps it has something to do with wanting to sound manly and stiff-upper-lipped. Thanks to Uncle Charles's recommendation, Rupert's exasperated parents sent him along to me, saying they couldn't understand a word he said. I suspect he thought this tiresome, unnecessary and even humiliating though he is too polite to say so. He is a nice boy (he once washed up my neglected breakfast things) and he has become interested in the workings of the human voice and the formation of language. Since he wants to become a lawyer, he is beginning to understand that speech is a useful tool and that he might as well learn to use it respectfully and effectively.

RAYMOND and Veronica have asked me to meet them in the park this morning and then go home with them for lunch. They are professional musicians – pianist and violinist respectively – and Veronica has just composed a piece for violin and piano they want me to hear. They are a nice, casual, untidy pair and I'm fond of them, but I mustn't stay with them too long for I still have a few lessons to prepare for tomorrow. A walk in the sunshiny park, followed by a bread-and-cheese lunch and some music, will be very pleasant.

I'll go and put on my coat.

FETTINGTON COURT

AT some schools visiting teachers are treated like resident staff. At others they are regarded as tiresome intruders who disrupt the timetable and don't belong to the community. At Fettington Court they are cossetted as though they were influential prospective parents.

A hire-car of the type used for weddings and funerals wafts me from the station along three miles of country road, past the lodge and up the drive through the timbered park to the eighteenth-century house.

The front door is open. I cross the hall under the scornful eyes of the Fettington forebears whose portraits regard their old home from a feudal past, while, I understand, the last of their line dwindles his old age away in a private hotel in Hove. I knock at the drawing-room door.

"Come in," calls a light voice and I make what I always hope is an Entrance.

Mrs Lumley-Stanford floats gently towards me. Her pale grey dress hangs mistily about her and her fair, faintly silvered hair hovers about her bland face. She holds out a hand for me to touch (shake it and it would, I believe, crumble into powder) and murmurs a greeting.

I sink into a sofa so deep that I have difficulty in

. . . my latest treasure

keeping my feet on the floor, while she drifts to a Chippendale chair by the rosewood table, touching the bell for coffee to be brought as she does so.

Believing me to be as sensitive and cultured as herself, Mrs Lumley-Stanford flatters me by leaving most of her sentences unfinished, as though she trusts to my intuition to complete them. Her trust is misplaced for I seldom have any idea what we are supposed to be talking about, but I fix on a smile in the hope that it will be taken for appreciative understanding, and try to look at once alert and relaxed.

Suddenly I catch sight of a picture over the bureau that was not there last week. It depicts a red triangle in mortal combat with a nude black woman of enormous proportions who, in spite of her superior size, seems to be getting the worst of the battle. She has lost an eye and the remaining one has been pushed into her nose. One arm is painfully swollen, the other shrivelled to a stick.

"You are looking at my latest treasure," croons Mrs Lumley-Stanford. "Terribly exciting . . . mm?"

"Yes indeed," I reply; "quite extraordinary."

A maid brings coffee on a silver tray. On the lawn beyond the tall windows about twenty girls stroll or stand about in the autumn sunshine. They wear green skirts and round-necked, collarless yellow blouses. Mrs Lumley-Stanford follows my glance and, smiling, says as she has so often said before, "Dear young things! Green and golden. I adore flowers and children are . . ."

I finish my delicious coffee and rise to go. There is a familiar sinking of the stomach and stiffening of the sinews as I prepare to meet my first class, a gang of pampered toughs called the 'Daffodils'. (Each class here bears the name of a flower.) Mrs Lumley-Stanford often tells me how much they enjoy their work with me. Purest humbug. And what does she mean by 'work'?

Am I really as bad a teacher as these children make

me feel? I wonder how the rest of the staff get on with them. Perhaps they have them all working quietly and purposefully within seconds of entering the room. I have met none of the other mistresses so I don't know. There have been moments when the Daffodils have shown some interest, but the habit of blasé boredom is strong and to admit to enjoying anything that calls for physical, mental or imaginative effort is a social solecism.

Janet Silcott is always the first to notice if she and her fellows are not decently bored. At once she droops into an attitude of lethargy and drawls, "Oh, Lord, this is *feeble*! Can't we do something decent for a change?" The others quickly follow her lead. "Feeble!" they moan. "Soppy . . . infantile . . ." I have tried all the text-book methods of approach and many less orthodox. Reference to Mrs Lumley-Stafford, besides being an admission of failure, would be useless for she is obviously even more ineffectual than I am. The children laugh at her and, even within my hearing, call her 'Loony Lum'. At my first interview she told me she didn't believe in compulsion or scolding of any kind. All must be happy collaboration. She certainly wouldn't approve of the reactionary methods I sometimes use during this dreaded forty-five minutes. I have been known to shout, stamp and use unseemly language. Naturally I do none of these things too often or they would cease to be effective but, having once let fly a well-timed bellow, it is generally possible to use the surprised silence that follows it to speak in more restrained tones and to get the gang to apply themselves to some work. Even Janet can be quelled in this way and, once she is chastened into laying aside her protective belligerence, the others follow suit and even sometimes dare to admit they are enjoying themselves.

Janet is twelve, with large, bold, heavily-lashed eyes and a full-lipped, sulky mouth. She has a certain cunning but little real intelligence and, aware of this, sneers at

8

everything she thinks beyond her capabilities and suspects everything within her grasp of being childish. Yet, in a room full of children, it is Janet one notices first, even in the few seconds before she opens her mouth, and her malicious comments on her class-mates are uncomfortably apt.

No bells are rung at Fettington Court and, although this is a peaceful arrangement, it is difficult not to keep glancing at my watch, an action which shatters the concentration of any class, however absorbed in either work or rebellion. However, a surreptitious squint shows that I can now bring the lesson to an end.

For the next lesson I climb the wide and curving staircase to the Snowdrops' room. If I did not already know where to find them, the shouts and screams of these little dears would guide me. As I open the door into what must once have been a principal bedroom, the din hits me full in the face and for a moment I am stunned. Every child is yelling and most of them are hurling chairs and tables against the walls, to clear a space for their drama lesson with me. Rosalie, as usual, bursts into loud lamentations as someone accidentally hits her over the head with a chair leg. She is one of those unlucky people who are always getting bumped and pushed and knocked over, and she never learns either to avoid these mishaps or to put up with them.

When at last they notice me, the children make no less noise but merely direct it towards me in squealing requests to do this, that or the other exercise they have enjoyed in the past. I keep quiet and wait till the tumult and the shouting dies and Rosalie's wails are reduced to an occasional doleful sniff.

The half-hour passes quickly. These seven-year-olds know none of the rhymes and stories and have played none of the games of make-believe taught to their children by more enlightened parents, so I try to make up to them, as far as I can, for all they have missed and are missing at home. Their response is gratifyingly enthusiastic. At the end of the lesson they carry the chairs and tables back into place very quietly, for fear of arousing the sleeping dragon who might otherwise rush in on them. Rosalie falls over with a bump but refrains from letting out a yell. I creep out of the room.

After a private lesson with a mentally retarded child who tells me that 'foam' is the thing you use when you ring up your friends, it is time for lunch and, having repaired the ravages to my face and hair wrought by the morning's battle, I return to the drawing-room.

To my surprise Mrs Lumley-Stanford has a young man with her. "My son Adrian," she breathes by way of introduction. He is exquisite, with golden hair, large greenish eyes and an insignificant chin. His conversation, though concerned with people I don't know, is easier to follow than his mother's, for every sentence is carefully constructed and meticulously enunciated. However, comprehension is unnecessary since he doesn't speak to me and I am left free to concentrate on the cold salmon and delicious salad before me. After the *bombe surprise* we smoke Balkan Sobranie cigarettes with our black coffee.

As I rise to go to my next class, the beautiful Adrian gets to his feet, but he continues to talk to his mother without pause and merely directs a slight smile my way as I leave the room. I suppose I should be grateful for even that small courtesy.

The afternoon is less trying than the morning. There are more private lessons and a session with the Roses. These are sophisticated young women with pleasant manners. One or two of them have brains and ability and are quite keen to use them. Some are wrapped in an impenetrable fog. The rest are amiable and of average intelligence. I often wonder whether, when they were Daffodils, they

10

were as insufferable as the Janet crowd and whether the present Daffodils will become polite and respectable when they are promoted to the Roses.

The Roses are seldom complete. Nearly every week one or two girls are away, attending weddings or dances, or have gone with their parents for short holidays abroad. Quite often the whole lot of them have been taken up to London by Mrs Lumley-Stanford to a concert, a play or a picture exhibition. They stay at school only when there is nothing better to do elsewhere, and some of them have even become rather bored by these too frequent cultural excursions. None of them has any idea of doing anything in particular when she leaves school so they regard the acquisition of any knowledge or skill as utterly pointless.

Towards the end of the lesson Susanna Davidson comes in with a message from Mrs Lumley-Stanford who has to entertain some parents at teatime and would like me to have tea with the staff instead of in the drawing-room. I am glad of this, partly because I always feel too gross for the other-worldly atmosphere in which Mrs L-S is suspended and partly because I am anxious to meet the other members of her staff.

At my request, one of the girls leads me to the staff-room. We cross a cobbled yard to the old stables which have been converted into staff quarters. I am shown into a small, dark room, crammed with battered wooden chairs, a large stained and scratched mahogany table and two or three desks littered with papers. At one of these a tired-looking, middle-aged woman sits, correcting exercise books. Her hair, face and clothes are of a uniform beige. In one of two whiskery basket-chairs sits a dark young woman piling more orange lipstick onto her already brilliant mouth. I introduce myself and explain my presence. The elder of the two, Miss Richards, greets me and introduces herself and Miss Green. Neither of them is exactly unmannerly but they regard me with an air of mingled boredom and hostility which I find unnerving. Miss Green indicates the other basket chair which accepts me protestingly and snags my stocking.

There is a moment's uncomfortable silence and then the door is kicked open by a stout little body carrying a tray laden with thick white cups and saucers, a decorated jug and a dented metal teapot. She dumps the tray down on the table and pours herself out a cup. She doesn't notice me at first but when Miss Richards introduces us she beams in a friendly way and brings me the cup. She is Miss Milner.

Other mistresses come in and help themselves from the tray. I don't take in their names. They look at me as though I were a creature from another planet and, indeed, I feel decidedly foreign as I sip the bitter brew and remember the scented tea and thin bread-and-butter which is generally my fare in the drawing-room. A tin of weary biscuits is handed round.

The staff are all talking now but not to me. Miss Green has the kind of low, harsh voice that cuts through general conversation like a rook's through a chatter of sparrows. "Richy's just been telling me that Lady Lum's taking twenty of the brats up to the Queen's Hall on Friday," she says. "More bloody culture."

There are startled looks in my direction.

"It really is rather difficult sometimes," says Miss Richards apologetically. "The children miss so much of their school work because of all these expeditions."

I assure her it's difficult for me too, not only because so many lessons are missed but also because, when they *are* here, the girls seem unwilling to settle down to steady work.

"Work!" snorts Miss Green. "They don't know the meaning of the word. What with Glyndebourne, the Tate, the Old Vic, the Queen's Hall, these kids have done everything by the time they leave school except acquire a rudimentary education. And besides all the gallivanting they do with Lady Lum, there are all the social functions with their parents she lets them go to. They come back from those so insufferably superior they can hardly bring themselves to speak to us humble wage-earners."

The grumbling becomes general. It is not the usual superficial sort of grouse most of us teachers indulge in at times, but the deep-seated discontent of women who feel they are wasting their time, their talents and their energy. There is a groan when the name of Janet Silcott is mentioned and when I express an urge to do her actual bodily harm, everyone admits to a like desire.

Throughout all this indiscreet talk Miss Richards becomes increasingly nervous. She is probably afraid I shall report it in full to Mrs L-S. Having heard that I am a fellow sufferer, the others seem less suspicious. The youngest mistress is teased about the exquisite Adrian who has evidently paid her some attention. She is a particularly pretty girl.

"If you play your cards right, Paddy," says Miss Green, "you'll be installed in a plushy Chelsea flat with nothing to do but adore him – unless, of course, you'd like to go into partnership with your mother-in-law."

"I'd sooner cut my throat," says Paddy.

The plump Miss Milner asks what I had for lunch today and there is an awed silence as I describe the menu. They tell me that the staff had underdone, cold, fat mutton, tinned beetroot and soggy potatoes, followed by one or two dried apricots and custard, and that this was no worse than their usual lunch.

When I come out into the sunshine again, I feel that, far from enjoying them, the delicacies of Lady Lum's table will henceforth choke me.

After two more private lessons it is time to go. I pass through the hall under the proud eyes of the Fettington ancestors and sink, exhausted, into the waiting car. The flat green countryside spins soothingly by. At the little station I find a corner seat in the train and go straight to sleep. If my mouth falls open I'm past caring.

CRANSTEAD SCHOOL – 1

A cool, grey day, threatening rain. All the same, by the time I have climbed the hill from the station, carrying my caseful of books, I am far too hot. I scrunch down the short drive, between the laurels, and the smell of cabbage and plimsolls hits me as I open the stained-glass front door and cross the linoleum to the cloakroom where I hang my mackintosh.

The school is at prayers and presently I hear the clanging of the ancient piano as Miss Emily pounds out the opening bars of the hymn, and then the voices of the children waver into 'Lead us, Heavenly Father, lead us', lugubrious and breathy.

I creep along to the cloakroom where I am to take my first lesson. The hymn whimpers to an end, with only a few voices bothering to join in the Amen, and then there is the murmur of the Lord's Prayer, with one high, very young voice shriller and slower than the rest. Presently the door opens and the piano crashes into one of the three marches in Miss Emily's repertoire. Feet march in time across the linoleum and pound, helter-skelter, up the stairs. Some march down the passage to my classroom. Children in purple gym-slips and white shirts with purple ties surge in, intone a choral "Good morning, Miss

15

Garth,'' and go to sit at the battered desks, whispering and giggling.

This is a bright little bunch, delighted with the meagre twenty minutes of a lesson less formal than those that fill the rest of their timetable, and always clamouring to have it prolonged. Indeed, it's difficult to get far with them, partly because the lesson is so short and partly because they are unaccustomed to using either imagination or controlled speech and both have to be roused from inertia every week.

Break is at 10.45. A bell clangs and children from every classroom rush to the dining-room, gulp down milk from chipped white enamel mugs, and run out to scream on the bare patch that was once a lawn. I go to the sitting-room to join the other grown-up people.

Miss Rook has a little yellow, anxious face with wire-rimmed glasses clinging to it and sparse, grey hair scraped back into a knob. She believes that comfort is weakness and weakness a sin, that children should be taught to behave nicely, write neatly and recite correctly the multiplication tables and large slices of the Bible. Thus equipped, they are ready to face Life – which she herself has never so much as glanced at. Nevertheless, she knows the world has changed. Dwindling pupils, higher staff salaries, accumulating tradesmen's bills make it all too evident. Grimly, she cuts down on food, on fuel, on staff. Where before she accepted only the children of gentlefolk, she must now take those of farmers and shopkeepers, some of whom (oh, horror!) speak with the local accent. She puts on a special voice when she speaks to these children – rather loud and slow, with an extra-kind inflexion, as though they were deaf and not quite all there.

I gather it is mainly because of that infectious local accent (even the well-born children are catching it, she tells me) that I have been engaged, and it is because times are hard that she can afford to have me here for only one morning a week and for the shortest possible lessons, so short as to be practically useless.

The gentler Miss Emily would, given the chance, gladly succumb to the sin of self-indulgence so scrupulously shunned by her sister. I have seen her slip three lumps of sugar into her cup of tea and, in cold weather, she pulls a chair close to the grate and stretches blue hands to the smouldering lumps of coal while Miss Rook, her hands equally blue, stands by the open window. Miss Emily looks after the house and the meals, bandages grazed knees and teaches music and needlework. She carries one or two sweets in her pocket, to pop into the mouths of crying children. She loves all the girls so much (especially the little ones) that, although they must think her a funny old thing, they can't help being fond of her. Miss Rook is the younger of the two sisters by several years, but she is the headmistress and the dominant one, so it is Miss Emily who is called by her Christian name.

In a few minutes we are joined by Miss Ringwood, a bony woman who has been teaching at Cranstead for some twenty years. Winter and summer she wears an olive-green cardigan and immensely long brogues. Some remnant of her last meal always adheres to one of her large teeth and her constant smile never quite reaches her eyes. She strides up to the school every day from her cottage in the village. Miss Emily once told me that she lives with a slightly dotty stepmother and a crippled brother.

Nobody sits down at break. We stand about with our cups while Miss Ringwood tells us that it was such a lovely day yesterday and today it's quite chilly. Miss Emily and I eagerly agree and glance disapprovingly at the dull sky.

Young Mrs Williams rushes in, red-headed and freckled. She exclaims with delight at the cup of tepid tea awaiting her, tells us enthusiastically how sweet Molly is, how clever Joan was this morning and how hard poor Barbara tries. The room seems to light up. The Misses Rook straighten themselves and their eyes almost shine, Miss Ringwood displays an even larger area of teeth than usual and I wonder how I could ever doubt that teaching is an exhilarating adventure.

Miss Rook picks up the hand-bell, leans out of the window and jangles it violently. The screaming children scream even louder and dash into the house. Miss Rook darts into the hall and hushes them. Silence is immediate. Screaming, hushing, quiet. Though I am here for only one day a week, this must be a daily routine. There is no attempt to establish a habit of silence once the bell is rung, though there is never any disobedience when Miss Rook demands quiet. Her authority is of the pecking kind. Rules are made but are always broken unless she is on hand to enforce them and it never seems to have occurred to her that the school could be run in any other way.

For the rest of the morning I rush from classroom to classroom. No sooner have I started a lesson than it is time to finish it and go on to another. There are also private lessons in the sitting-room and, as these are paid for as 'extras' by the parents (Miss Rook nabbing twenty per cent of my fees), they are rather longer.

Miss Emily is always very concerned that I do not stay to lunch, but I am only too thankful to escape. The narrow tables, covered with stained oil-cloth, are laid with tin spoons and forks and are not inviting. Miss Emily cooks with the kitchen door open and the house is filled with the smell of boiled cod and greens. As I pass through the hall on my way to the cloakroom, I see her – tiny, white-haired and determined – piling the watery contents of enormous saucepans onto plates which will be carried into the dining-room a good ten minutes before the children are summoned by more jangling of the bell (as I have heard the children complain), so the food is always cold.

. . . jangles it violently

There is a fine rain falling now. I pull on my mackintosh, run out of the house and down the hill, just in time to catch my train.

STANDISH LODGE – 1

LUNCH is nearly over and the one hundred and ten boarders and day-girls are making about the same amount of noise as most of the parents would make at a cocktail party. One or two of the younger and slower eaters are still scraping up the last of the batter pudding and syrup. Everyone at Standish Lodge is expected to behave politely so we mostly do, especially at table. We are supposed to make conversation, but today I've given up trying to talk through the clamour and anyway one of my neighbours seems to be wrapped in a day-dream, while the other is giggling away with the child beside her, so I feel free to sit quiet and watch the girls of all shapes and sizes on either side of the long table at which I preside.

Miss James tinkles her bell. There is a sudden hush, followed by the scraping and squealing of chairs as we all stand. Grace is said and then, table by table, the children file out of the dining-room in silence while we on the staff wait for them to go.

Miss James is at her usual place by the door, watching the procession. Tall, well corseted, faintly smiling, she must be the only person in the school never to be laughed at, disliked or loved, but always respected. The bay window is largely filled by Miss Browne whose abundant torso is supported by slender legs and who now gazes into space and sucks her teeth. Near her, little Miss Egginton enjoys a surreptitious whisper with one of the prefects and, from across the room, Mademoiselle jangles her bangles and gives me the suspicion of a wink. The rest of us stand about in characteristic attitudes, as unobtrusively as possible.

When the last girl has disappeared, Miss James and Miss Browne repair to their sitting-room for coffee. We, the humbler creation, drift along to the staff-room for cups of tea.

Remembering my own school days, I imagine the children have us neatly pigeon-holed in categories of Jolly Decent, Not Bad and Ghastly and that, within these categories, the idiosyncrasies of each one of us are minutely observed and mimicked with varying degrees of accuracy. The sum of each set of habits and mannerisms adds up to a 'being' (I will not say human) which is distinct and complete as far as the girls are concerned, but which differs a good deal from the way we see ourselves and each other. Each version is partly true, but we alter it according to which side of the staff-room door we find ourselves – some of us, I believe, quite unconsciously.

Now the staff-room door shuts. 'Zelly' (Mademoiselle), that stickler for proper manners, throws herself on the sofa, rubbing her stomach and moaning, "Oh, mon Dieu! That pooding! My pipes! My pipes!" 'Eggy' (Miss Egginton), for whom there is no world outside Standish Lodge, settles herself at the table with her tea and her friend, Margaret Anderton, to discuss late developers in general and IVB's Molly Parkin in particular. Margaret blinks at her through thick glasses and fingers the pile of exercise books she was hoping to correct during the lunch break. Rachel Strong, the bane of the slothful on the hockey field and in the gym, curls up in a chair, with a cigarette and a copy of *Movie Mag*.

Young Phillipa Gedge comes over to ask me wistful questions about London. She is convinced that my life there is daringly unconventional and sophisticated and she gets such a kick out of this belief that I take pains to think up another instalment of my romantic 'True Confessions' story to recount every week. She doesn't quite swallow all my wilder inventions but she enjoys them just the same.

Fraulein Trudi Hartmann sits near us on a pouffe, showing a large expanse of mottled thigh between her pale blue drawers and lisle stockings. She sucks up her tea more quietly than usual because she wants to hear what I am saying so that she can acquire merit by retailing the more colourful passages to Miss Browne who has a ready ear for scandal but, to give her her due, enough sense to administer large pinches of salt when its source is not reliable.

There is to be a staff meeting at two o'clock, so at five minutes to two Zelly pulls herself together and primly takes up a bit of pink embroidery, Rachel stuffs the magazine into her desk and sits with uncrossed legs and her knitting, Eggy flutters round the room, tidying things away so that no one will ever be able to find them again, and Phillipa idly turns the pages of a text book, though I feel sure her mind is on more exciting matters. 'Frauly' (Fraulein Hartmann) heaves herself off the pouffe, asks me how to pronounce the words formidable and hospitable and then tells me of all the well-educated people she knows who pronounce them the other way.

Punctually at two o'clock Miss James taps gently on the door and comes in with Miss Browne who has a quick look round to see what we are all doing. We go and sit at the table.

Eggy opens the proceedings in the usual way by complaining about the lavatory doors being left open. We all look suitably concerned, as though we had never before had our attention drawn to this regrettable habit. Frauly remarks that, in Germany, open lavatory doors would not be tolerated. Margaret, who is good at lettering, offers to make SHUT THE DOOR notices to pin up in all lavatories, but Miss Browne squashes the idea at once by pointing out that, after two days, nobody would bother to read them. Miss James says she will make another appeal when the school assembles for prayers.

The next point is raised by Miss Browne (known to those of her colleagues who do not enjoy her favour as 'Flannel Feet') who, leaning earnestly across the table – thus obliterating a large area of its surface – calls the attention of the meeting to the bad language in vogue amongst the gently-nurtured young ladies of Standish Lodge. She heard some examples of this emanating from IIIA dormitory the other night, at an hour when its inmates should, in any case, have been lapped in silence and slumber. She also ''happened to hear'' rude words shouted from behind the shut door of the Senior Common-room. Much as we dislike Flannel Feet's eavesdropping propensities, we all long to know what was actually said, though none of us dares to ask. Rachel, blushing furiously, reports an outburst of temper on the hockey field when, having received a sharp blow on the ankle, the injured party was heard to yell "Damn and blast you, Jean!" Pressed by Eggy for the name of the offender, Rachel reluctantly reveals that it was Daphne Ryder. This annoys Flannel Feet who believes that Daphne can do no wrong, and she and Miss James embark on an antiphonal account of Daphne's unsatisfactory home life which is alone responsible for any irregularities of behaviour. One or two of the other staff, who consider the child to be insufferably precocious and conceited, ignore these excuses, and their criticisms, though apparently disinterested, are far from charitable. Daphne's character is ruthlessly analysed and condemned. This onslaught can be of no benefit to the victim but it certainly throws light on the characters of her mentors and

*Miss Brown calls the attention of the meeting
to the bad language in vogue*

tormentors. In the excitement of the discussion, the sins of IIIA dormitory are forgotten and soon a distant bell summons us to our classrooms for afternoon lessons. We have achieved as much as we usually do at staff meetings.

AFTER my last class there is an hour to spare before I have to walk the half-mile to the station to catch a train back to London. I go and sit in the garden in the autumn sunshine and half-heartedly start to prepare tomorrow's lessons. A confusion of music floats out from the open windows of the house. A Mozart piano concerto and a Beethoven sonata do brilliant battle. A potential violinist saws away on open strings. There is an occasional scream from an unruly clarinet and a laborious pounding out of Schumann's 'Soldier's March' from one of the more elderly pianos. I find these mingled sounds surprisingly pleasing and peaceful, particularly as they are accompanied by the whirr of a distant lawn-mower and the drone of a sleepy bee. The school resounds with ordered activity. It is a complete world, untroubled by outside events. For a moment I forget the passions that seethe beneath the surface in this as in other schools, and wish I were cloistered here as a resident.

I think of my colleagues, so diverse in character and outlook. In spite of this diversity – or perhaps because of it – I realise that Miss James has chosen her staff pretty shrewdly. Her large brown eyes seem to perceive in people some hidden worth not always apparent to the rest of us. She trusts her judgment and is seldom disappointed. Thinking of Flannel Feet and Frauly, I admit this with a certain reluctance.

I shut my eyes and the sun shines red through the lids. How can I get Cynthia to abandon that mincing, genteel accent, no doubt inherited from her parents? Is it possible that Babs can be as stupid as she seems or is she merely lazy? The Fourths are a delight to teach and they are ready

26

for more ambitious work than I have so far given them. Bridget intends to produce part of the Coventry Cycle, for Christmas, with the Seniors, if I will please give her a bit of help if she needs it. Oh, *gladly*, bless the child!

The town-hall clock strikes the half-hour. It's time I made my way to the station.

RINGER'S END – 1

DOROTHY Andrews sets me down at the gate because she wants to take the school car along to the garage for petrol. The sun is out and, when I walk round the corner of the drive, I see the Headmistress, Miss Tarrant, sitting on the front doorstep, peeling apples. Her massive bare legs are plum-coloured and, on this mild September day, she wears a voluminous frock of handwoven shot-silk – blue and green – and a necklace of large coloured beads.

"Good heavens!" she bawls when she sees me. "You here already? I didn't realise it was so late."

She gives a low but penetrating hoot which is almost immediately answered by a three-note whistle. Mrs Minton appears at the door, a vision of dainty femininity in her flowered overall and with pale blue ribbon round her curly head. Her hair, newly gilded, gleams in the sun, her blue eyes are perfectly round and, were it not for the slight bagginess round the jaws and throat, no one would believe her to be a day over forty.

"Be a lamb," booms Miss Tarrant, "and take these apples into the kitchen for me. I've got Senior History now."

"Right you are, ducky," pipes Mrs Minton. She takes the bowls of apples and apple-peel while Miss Tarrant

. . . the Headmistress, Miss Tarrant

heaves herself to her feet and strides into the house. Mrs Minton gives a welcoming titter in my direction and disappears after her.

I follow them in, hang my coat among the mackintoshes in the hall and go along to the English room to take over the Fifth Form from Ruth Thomas who has been taking them for Eng.lit. Ruth is a plain, determined young woman, who, having come down from Oxford a year ago, knows all there is to be known about 'education', 'teaching method', 'psychology' and, of course, 'literature', and is only too willing to instruct the rest of us in these subjects.

As I come in, she is reading aloud a D.H. Lawrence short story in strident tones and the girls are huddled or draped over their desks like bundles of old clothes. Some appear to be asleep, one or two are scribbling over their blotting-paper, one is tracing a map and another reading a magazine. They are a grubby, untidy lot but I know them to be pleasant, friendly and teachable.

Ruth departs and I give my lesson. Then the Fifth Form drift out and the Third Form rush in like a hurricane. After that comes the sober Sixth Form and then it's time for lunch.

For this meal the staff assemble in the kitchen with its huge table and mighty Aga. Two of the senior girls dish out cold beef, salad and potatoes and three or four of the younger ones take the loaded plates to the clamorous mob in the dining-room next door, while we settle down at the table. During lunch, Miss Tarrant booms, Mrs Minton twitters and we just eat.

". . . so I told Diana's doting Mum that, if she didn't like our ways, she could take her little darling off to a more refeened establishment," bellows Miss Tarrant through a mouthful of potato. Mrs Minton squeals with delight and turns her wide blue eyes upon us, to make sure we appreciate our Headmistress's daring.

"Binkie darling!" she shrieks, "you really are the absolute limit!"

Girls return with piles of dirty plates and, having dumped them on the draining-board, start serving stewed apples and custard.

"Be a lamb, Tiddles," says Miss Tarrant, "and fetch some of that cold rice pudding for the twins."

"Oo yes, apples don't agree with them, por ickle fings!" Mrs Minton picks up two bowls from the dresser and scampers off to the larder.

Ruth glowers at her plate, Dorothy glances at me and makes a face of repressed nausea, Miss Robinson gives an ingratiating little laugh and Mrs Sims hastily starts to tell Miss Tarrant about one of the children's pet rabbits. She is interrupted by Miss Tarrant who suddenly leaves the table and shouts, "Your turn to be washer-up, Robby, my dear."

Miss Robinson smiles anxiously, fetches her little pink apron from a hook on the door and goes to the sink, trying to look as though she didn't loathe the task before her. The rest of us collect smelly tea-towels and stand about, waiting to dry the dishes. It is quite unnecessary for so many of us to be in attendance but nobody likes to back out. 'Robby' hates washing up so much that she forces herself to be more meticulous than any of us, and the operation takes ages. First, each item in turn is held under a running tap. Then it is plunged into soapy water so hot that she can hardly bear to fish it out and mop it, and keeps sucking in her breath every time she scalds herself. Finally, each separate piece is rinsed in clear water. It is only then, having worked ourselves up into a frenzy of impatience, that we all fall upon the first single spoon that is ready to be wiped. Robby's labour is rendered futile by the filthiness of the tea-towels which spread a rich layer of grease and germs on everything they touch.

Towards the end of this ritual Miss Tarrant re-heats the

morning's coffee, pours it into coloured mugs and, when the last saucepan has been scoured, washed, rinsed, wiped and put on its shelf, we light cigarettes and settle down to a tepid drink. Miss Tarrant and Mrs Minton take their coffee to the drawing-room (a dark red mug bearing the letter B for 'Binkie' and a pale blue one with T for 'Tiddles') and the kitchen seems strangely quiet and empty without them, though we now talk more easily.

Robby, having washed and re-washed her hands, sits bolt upright, sipping her coffee and blotting her lips with a ragged, lace-edged handkerchief between each sip. Poor little Robby! Her creased and pointed face is yellowish from years spent in West Africa as a missionary, suffering hardship, disease and, I believe, terror. She doesn't speak of these experiences but we have somehow got to know a little about them, I suppose through Mrs Minton. The privations she endured have made her extraordinarily fastidious so that she is forever washing her clothes and her person and exhorting the children to do likewise. Of course they take no notice and, ignorant of her history, just laugh at her behind her back. Robby is timid, anxious to please and mortally afraid of losing her job which, she knows very well, has been given her mostly out of kindness and because she is a distant relation of Mrs Minton's. I believe she is not a bad teacher but her methods must be old fashioned by any standards and she is certainly out of place in such an unconventional establishment as Ringer's End.

Mrs Sims holds her mug in both hands and smiles lazily over it through half-closed eyes. It is understood that she is a widow. Her eight-year-old daughter, Priscilla, is at school here. 'Simmy' is like a large, well-fed cat. Her voice is low, soft and monotonous as a purr. She pads silently about on sandalled feet, curls her body into the most unsympathetic chairs, yawns and stretches with sensuous and feline pleasure. When she is with the little girls who are in her charge, she is like a mother cat with its kittens. They crowd round her, climb onto her lap, lean over her shoulder. And then, suddenly, she shakes them all off and starts some newly-invented game in which she and the children run all over the place.

I remember once seeing some photographs of a cat and a mouse who lived together in unnatural harmony. Simmy and Robby remind me of that pair. They are fundamentally incompatible, yet they have a sort of liking and respect for one another which, though it could never amount to real friendship, withstands many of the irritations of community life. Robby has had many experiences, but Simmy is the one with 'experience'. Robby has lived dangerously, but Simmy is the one with a 'past' – and, I suspect a 'present' too for she is not a resident here and has a rented cottage nearby. The anxious Baptist and the happy pagan are mutually gentle and trusting.

Dorothy Andrews can't stand either of them, though she is too polite to show her dislike. She is a tall, fair young woman of conventional views and habits, some of which she is able to waive as far as the children are concerned because of her admiration for the academically distinguished Miss Tarrant who, though unconventional in her approach to education, indulges in no adventures (as far as one can tell) other than those of the mind. Ruth and Dorothy sometimes get involved in fierce arguments about teaching, in the course of which Ruth becomes more and more supercilious and cold – being sure she is right – and Dorothy more and more heated and flustered, being certain she knows best. On the whole, however, the two are quite good friends.

This afternoon I have a drama class with the combined Third and Fourth forms. This has to be held in the entrance hall because there is no classroom big enough to take such a large number of children, particularly for an active lesson, and the assembly hall is occupied at this time by the orchestra. We can hear the strings grinding away at a Frank Bridge suite and the desperate voice of Mr Frake as he yells directions over the din. They seem to have been working at this particular piece for the past three terms, without noticeable improvement.

I start the lesson. The children are well away with a scene they have prepared for me. "Sign!" shout the Barons with one voice. There is a dramatic pause as the trembling King John moves slowly towards the table. It is a tense moment. Then, the door flies open and Mrs Minton trips in.

"So sorry, Miss Garth," she says brightly. "I didn't realise you were in here. Do you mind if I just ring up the butcher?"

The question is rhetorical. She goes to the telephone and, after asking how the butcher and his wife are keeping and how little Jimmy is getting on at his new school (enquiries answered in the fullest detail by Mr Padgers at the other end of the line), she goes on to complain of last week's liver and to place a long and complicated order. At last, with a merry "Good afternoon, Mr Padgers," sung on a major third, she replaces the receiver, turns to me with a winning smile and a further "*So* sorry, Miss Garth," and departs *con brio*, clicking the door smartly to behind her.

The children sigh and exchange glances which I carefully seem not to notice. We get down to work again. The first zest is lost but some life remains in what they were doing and they are just getting back into their stride when there is a ring at the front door bell. Five children immediately rush to see who is there. It is the postman, with a registered parcel. Having dealt with this, we return to the signing of Magna Carta.

A few minutes later Mr Frake emerges from the assembly hall, tiptoes past me with ostentatious discretion, and

. . . an explanatory spare violin string

creeps upstairs. Unfortunately he has left the door ajar so that we get the full benefit of the unsupervised orchestra, whose members break into loud chatter, bang the chairs about and produce blood-curdling cacophony from their instruments. I stride furiously in to restore order and silence and then return to quell my own class who are now smitten with the giggles. They have just got over the worst paroxysms when Mr Frake creeps down the stairs again, waves an explanatory spare violin string in my direction, and disappears into the assembly hall. This dumb crambo throws the children into renewed convulsions and I am bound to laugh myself, which releases their semi-suppressed mirth into a roar of delight. King John is as dead as Queen Anne.

At the appointed hour I send my children back to their classrooms. At the same time, the orchestra streams out of the assembly hall. Girls thunder upstairs, shouting to each other. Girls gallop down the passage, shouting to each other. Girls stand about, shouting to each other. Mr Frake and I wait for the hubbub to subside, shrugging our shoulders, exchanging sympathetic smiles, shaking our heads and making no attempt either to converse or to quieten the tumult. We know well enough that Miss Tarrant would frown upon any curbing of this natural exuberance between lessons, though I am sure she carries out her teaching in an atmosphere of quiet concentration.

When the hall is empty, Mr Frake and I go upstairs together. He is a small, quiet, ageing man with sparse hair and a neat, grey moustache. His shabby jacket falls from his narrow shoulders almost as though it were hanging from a hook, and his pockets bulge like panniers. He stares through rimless glasses so thick as to turn his eyes into pale puddles, and his gentle voice still carries the accent of his native Clapham. He is a retired orchestral musician who has always longed, not for the glory of the soloist, but for the satisfaction of what he calls "ongsomble playing". He dislikes teaching, "but there," he says, without self-pity, "we can't always choose what we do."

With a friendly nod he disappears into his music room. I go next door into one of the bathrooms, which is where I have to take my private lessons. In here, the voices of my pupils resound with deceptive splendour, but the walls are thin and we have to compete, first with a beginner scraping away on a 'cello, then with a violinist whose playing shows determination and breath-taking inaccuracy, followed by another fiddler who, after a few exercises, manages to divert Mr Frake from their mutual agony by easing him into conversation. When I hear his thin voice flowing on and on, I guess he is indulging his passion for musical reminiscence. All in all I daresay the declamations from the bathroom are more disturbing to Mr Frake and his pupils than the noises from the music-room are to me and mine.

When my last lesson is finished I go down for tea. Mr Frake has a tray sent up to him so that he can go on teaching without interruption. Some of the staff are already in the kitchen, including Miss Tarrant and Mrs Minton, together with Caesar, the ancient, fat and smelly spaniel. Miss Tarrant asks me how the drama lesson went and, when I start to tell her, she interrupts me with a "Widgey, widgey, my booful boy. Does you want your cuppa then, my precious? Doody-doody-doody then."

I give up. Miss Tarrant fills her cup with weak tea and puts it on the floor where Caesar noisily laps it up. Robby, watching this unhygienic performance, looks as though she were being tortured. She says nothing but moves unobtrusively to the sink to wash her cup yet again.

Miss Tarrant has two or three ways of dealing with problems and grumbles. If one of us raises a subject which calls for her decision or for some effective action, she at once starts to talk to someone else or to Caesar. Or she says, "That reminds me . . ." and produces a convenient red herring. If really cornered she says, "Yes, we shall have to think of something, shan't we?" and leaves the room in a hurry as though she had some urgent duty to attend to at that very moment. Exasperating though it is, this technique has something to commend it. For one thing it makes us all reluctant to make any complaint. For another, the problems she ignores often solve themselves or are settled between the rest of us. All the same, there are many simple ways by which the running of the school could be improved, if only Miss Tarrant could be persuaded to consider them.

Needless to say, Ruth Thomas started a campaign of reformation after she had been here barely half a term, and when she found she could get no backing from Miss Tarrant, took matters into her own hands. She organised a French table at lunchtime and went to preside over it, having an impeccable command of the language. Of course her absence from the kitchen was noticed and investigated and when she came in for coffee Miss Tarrant said, "By the way, Ruth, we won't have a French table if you don't mind. You can take French conversation during school hours and you and the children can have a rest from each other at lunchtime. Tiddles dear, would you be a lamb and run into Stongford this afternoon? I've a little list for you."

"But you see, Miss Tarrant," protested Ruth, "I thought if . . ."

"Doo-de-doo-de-*doo*, Caesar, my precious!" said Miss Tarrant.

After one or two of her other bright ideas had been disposed of in the same way, Ruth gave up trying to make any changes and consoled herself by telling the rest of us about them and by grumbling about the way everything is simply allowed to *drift*.

38

IT is time for me to leave. I rise and smile encouragingly at Mrs Minton who is supposed to drive me to the station.

"Oodles of time, my dear," she says, pouring herself another cup of tea. "You run and get your coat. I'll be with you in a trice."

I say my goodbyes, fetch my coat and wait in the hall. The minutes slide past and Mrs Minton still doesn't appear. I go back to the kitchen and find her sipping tea, throwing bits of biscuit to Caesar and telling Miss Tarrant how ghastly it is, the way children will keep leaving the lavvy doors open. (Haven't I heard this complaint somewhere before?) I stand waiting, getting very hot.

"Buck up, Tiddles," says Miss Tarrant, "this poor girl's waiting." Mrs Minton glances at her watch.

"Oodles of time, Binkie," she says; "don't fuss," and takes another sip of tea.

At last she gets up, powders her nose, goes out with me to the garage and, after four prolonged tugs at the starter, succeeds in squeezing just enough life out of the battery to get the car going. William (as she so wittily calls the senile Morris) backs violently into the drive. She looks at her watch.

"Heavens!" she exclaims with a giggle, "We've cut it a bit fine, haven't we! Hop in, dear. We shall have to step on it."

William lurches down the drive and into the road, narrowly missing a passing car. Mrs Minton celebrates the miss by a prolonged blast on the horn. She sits bolt upright, clutching the top of the wheel and keeping the car to the centre of the winding road. Round a bend we meet an old man on a bicycle. He topples into one bank and we scrape along the other. Mrs Minton waves gaily as we pass him.

"That's dear old Mr Bingham," she screams. "He's really far too old to ride a bike."

Our next encounter is with a young man in a sports car, also hugging the crown of the road.

"Keep to your own side!" yells Mrs Minton as we squeeze past with inches to spare. "Did you see that? Silly young ass . . . utterly irresponsible. *Really* these people!"

The rest of her remarks are lost as, with a fine disregard for other traffic, we swing into the main road and at once start up a steep hill. Not until the car is groaning and almost at a standstill does Mrs Minton grind into low gear, with a jolt that nearly sends me through the windscreen. At the top of the hill we turn into the station yard and all four wheels seem to leave the ground as we pull up. The train is in. Shaking with fury and terror I struggle to open the door, thanking Mrs Minton *so* much for bringing me in. Then I scramble out of the car, dash through the booking-office, across the platform and into the moving train.

Four bowler-hatted City gents peer at me over their newspapers and instantly recognise me as a third-class passenger polluting their first-class carriage. Further down the train I am able to find part of a seat between a peppermint-sucking woman and a bronchitic old man. Two children on the opposite seat enjoy themselves by kicking my shins and stamping on my toes. Somehow I manage to fish a whodunnit out of my case. I seek forgetfulness in its corpse-strewn pages.

ST JOSEPH'S CONVENT – 1

A tiresome train journey today, with two changes and then a longish ride in a country bus and a ten-minute walk to the convent.

The great grey building stands at the end of a drive winding between tall hedges and then opening onto a gravelled sweep by the front door, bordered by a well-kept lawn. I let myself into a dark hall smelling of furniture polish. Here I meet Sister Philip.

"Good morning, Miss Garth," she says, in surprised tones. "You weren't expecting we'd be having lessons today, were you? Did nobody tell you you wouldn't be needed?"

I am mystified.

"But it's Mother's Feast Day," she says in her soft Irish voice, and bursts out laughing to think that anyone should not know this.

I'm annoyed. All that wearisome journey for nothing and so many things I might have got on with at home. But it isn't Sister Philip's fault so I bite back my reproaches.

"Wait now till I bring you a cup of coffee," she says. "Go along to the reception room and rest yourself. To think of you coming all the way from London on a school holiday!"

Still laughing, she stumps off towards the kitchen, her back view like a black metronome, and I go on into the reception room. It is always dark in here, for the only window faces north onto a walled courtyard and the walls of the room are the colour of old mustard. There is heavy, Victorian furniture, a monumental upright piano and, on the table a vase of bronze chrysanthemums.

I remember the first time I saw Sister Philip. It was my second visit to St Joseph's so I didn't ring the bell but let myself in. At the far end of the hall the figure of Our Lady stands in an alcove, between vases of flowers and with a small electric bulb shining at her feet. As I moved towards the reception room I saw a dumpy little nun gliding and twirling before this figure, her arms outstretched. I thought I was perhaps witnessing some sort of devotional dance, so I started to tip-toe discreetly past. But as I came near, she turned, smiled and said good morning, though she continued her *pas seul*. It was then that I noticed a cloth beneath each of her feet. She was simply polishing the floor.

Sister Philip soon returns with a pot of coffee and a slice of fruit cake. Sister Mary is with her.

"Well now, imagine!" exclaims Sister Mary. "The terrible things you must be thinking of us, are you not? No, but really I should have told you there'd be no work done today. It just never crossed my mind and that's the truth. Sit down now and drink your coffee while it's hot."

How could anyone continue to feel cross after such a charming admission? I sit and pour my coffee. Sister Philip excuses herself and disappears. Sister Mary sits, tall and straight-backed, her hands hidden in her sleeves. Her face is ageless and calm.

"I dare say you'll be wanting to get home," she says, "but if you'd like to spend the day here now you've come, you're very welcome. They're playing an inter-house netball match at the moment, and this afternoon

. . . she continued her pas seul

we have a concert, just a little entertainment the girls have got up on their own. It's nothing very grand, you know, but we all enjoy it.''

Of course I say I shall be delighted to stay on and, when I have finished my coffee, we go down to the netball field to watch the match.

On the way I see Reverend Mother coming towards us and I gaily call out a good-morning to her while we are still some distance apart. She makes no sign of having heard my greeting but glides up, silent as a bat, withdrawing a thin hand from the folds of her habit, for me to shake. When she is quite close so that she need not rudely raise her voice as I did, she murmurs ''Good morning, Miss Garth,'' apologises for my unnecessary journey, repeats Sister Mary's invitation to stay for the concert, asks after my health and remarks on the inclement weather, pausing just long enough between each sentence for me to slip in an appropriate response. My voice sounds too loud, my manner seems brash. Altogether, she makes me feel as ladylike as a gangster's moll.

When we reach the field, children rush to get us chairs and I am pulled willingly away to sit with a group of twelve-year-olds whose friendly chatter is a relief after Mother's frigid courtesy.

A young priest has also come to watch the match. He is dark, with a bland, plump face and is almost eclipsed by a dozen little girls who sit on his knee, round his feet and on either side of him, all talking at once in shrill, excited voices that would never be tolerated by any nun. This is Father Ryan. I have never met him but I know he is the one who sometimes gathers some of the senior girls round a piano and pounds out selections from musical comedy for their entertainment and his own gratification. They come late to my lesson (and, presumably, to other lessons too), looking prim and innocent, and explain that they

44

have been 'detained' by Father Ryan. They miss quite a lot of work this way but, though the nuns must be well aware of these sessions, nothing is said. Father Ryan is, after all, a priest.

He and one or two other priests often visit the convent, some to take classes in 'doctrine' or psychology, others for the sake of the excellent meals which are served in their luxurious sitting-room by attentive nuns. Laughter and cigarette smoke billow out whenever the door is opened to admit yet another laden tray. At other times uproarious games are played with the younger children up and down the corridor outside the classroom in which I am trying to teach. One way and another, the convent gives the priests a lot of fun.

As usual, I lunch alone in the reception room, waited on by Sister Philip. So far as I can see, nuns don't eat. They evidently feel neither heat nor cold, so presumably they are never hungry either. Nor do they appear to suffer changes of mood. Mother is always frigid and correct, Sister Mary is always dignified and humorous, and Sister Philip always overflowing with cheerful kindliness. I have a smiling acquaintance with one or two of the others but there are several whose names I have never learnt. When I first came, all the nuns looked alike to me and I never knew them apart. Now I wonder how I could ever have confused them.

The only time I ever had a meal in the priests' room was on one of the Speech and Drama examination days. The convent insists that as many girls as possible enter for the graded exams set by one of the London colleges of Music and Drama, and my job is to prepare them for these. For my first two years at the convent, a lady examiner was sent to officiate and she and I lunched together in the reception room. The third year came a Man and, for all the fuss that was made of him, he might have been a Royal Personage. No priests were there that day, so the examiner and I were shown into their sitting-room. The table was set with the best silver and we were each given a glass of very sweet sherry, followed by a three-course meal such as one might expect at one of the better hotels. The examiner told me that he usually enjoyed this kind of hospitality at the various convents he visited.

Besides the annual examinations, the girls of St Joseph's also enter for one or two of the local competitive festivals, in the verse-speaking and prose-reading classes. They did this for years before I joined the staff for, as in many convents, a good deal of importance is attached to speech education and its application to the study of poetry and prose. I am in favour of these competitions for I feel it is good for the girls to learn something of the work of other schools (they are inclined to think themselves in every way superior to these) and to have their own work criticised by various adjudicators. Naturally, we are all delighted if any of our competitors bring back a medal, a cup or some certificates of merit, but at the first festival I went to, I was shocked to find that the nuns thought only of these trophies and not at all about the competitions themselves. High marks brought exclamations of delight, together with nods and becks and wreathèd smiles, while adverse criticism was received with head-shakings and groans, all clearly visible and audible to other competitors, their doting families and the rest of the audience. Given this example by the nuns, the girls felt free to show still more violent reactions, much to my embarrassment. Before the next festival I delivered a stern homily to every class (I could hardly lecture the nuns on proper behaviour) on 'How to Win', 'How to Lose' and how to accept criticism with at least a show of respect, even when the adjudicator is believed to be talking nonsense.

But to return to the Mother's Feast Day entertainment. We assemble in the hall. The nuns sit at the back and I sit in the row in front of them with those of the senior girls who are not taking part in the show. Two or three priests sit in the front row – of course – and the other rows are occupied by children of the younger forms, all bubbling with excitement.

Rosemary, the Head Girl, announces each item (briefly and clearly, I am pleased to note) but, as the programme proceeds, I sink into ever-deepening gloom. There are several sentimental Irish songs rendered by two intrepid soloists with a good deal of emotional swooping and an occasional breakdown when words are forgotten. There are recitations of sweetly pretty verses (culled from calendars and magazines perhaps?) imperfectly memorised and delivered archly or mechanically, according to the temperament of the speaker. There are one or two laborious piano pieces and an original sketch about a tea-party at which an unwelcome guest arrives, is cold-shouldered and leaves in a huff. Most of the dialogue is provided by the prompter who is probably also the author, and the actors (in funny hats, insecure moustaches and borrowed great-coats) giggle their way through the thing, to the delight of the audience.

Each item is received with enthusiastic applause. The nuns keep exclaiming how well everyone is doing. The children clap loud and long because it is fun to be allowed to make that much noise for once. I manage a reluctant clap because I am a guest and no doubt Mother has her eye on me.

The show drags on and I am beginning to plan an escape when at last it dwindles to an end. We heave our aching behinds off the hard chairs and clear our throats for the singing of the National Anthem, played all wrong by Jennifer Lenton. The nuns troop out in single file and I follow them till they disappear through the door which leads to their private quarters. Dear Sister Philip darts back to promise me tea and I go alone to the reception room to wait for it.

"Now, wasn't that a fine concert!" she exclaims when she returns with the tray. "That Susan, now, wasn't she just lovely with 'The Rose of Tralee'? And little Victoria, standing up to say her pome as clear as clear!"

She leaves me to my tea and presently Rosemary comes in, ostensibly to look for some music but really to ask my opinion of the concert. I praise the clarity of her announcements and say no more. Knowing pretty well what I must be thinking, she blushes.

"Well, I know it was terrible but it's only for the nuns. They enjoyed it. They always do."

I am disappointed and angry and wonder what I have taught these children all this time, but I manage some sort of a smile and promise to discuss the matter next week, in class. Meanwhile, I have a train to catch.

Sister Mary comes to the front door to see me off. She shrugs her shoulders slightly and gives me a sad smile. She says little but it is enough to make me realise she understands how I feel and even, perhaps, feels as I do. It is only when I am in the bus that I remember I never sought out Mother to thank her for her hospitality and never congratulated her on her Feast Day – if that is what one is supposed to do.

It is strange to be a non-Catholic lay teacher at a convent. I am an outsider, cut off from the most essential part of convent life and even from the workings of its school. Girls are sometimes expelled but I am never told why or when. They simply disappear and their friends, not the nuns, tell me they have gone. Rosemary's younger sister, Joyce, was one of them – a quiet, inoffensive girl who ran away after bullies in the dormitory had repeatedly attacked her. That, at least, is Rosemary's story and I have no reason to disbelieve her.

I dare say I shouldn't listen to all the tales I am told by the girls. I receive them guardedly and with what tact I can muster, but I allow them to be told. For one thing,

I need to know what is going on. For another, there is no other grown-up person in whom they can confide. Occasionally, a sentimental friendship develops between one of the nuns and a Catholic girl or a would-be convert (would-be on the girl's side; the nuns make no attempt to convert their Protestant pupils) but for neither Catholic nor non-Catholic is there an unshockable ear. As I am ready to provide one – in the course of private lessons – I hear a good deal, not only about school matters but also about clothes and films and boys and unsuitable careers, all the things that are out of a nun's world.

But even the rebels are fond of many of the nuns, though I sense a bitter distrust and dislike of Mother which even I will not allow to be expressed.

I wonder whether I shall ever feel at ease with her. Whenever we meet I say something clumsy and she accepts it with a chilly courtesy more devastating than any reproof. One October I remarked on the wonderful colours of the fallen leaves on the garden paths and she at once apologised for their untidiness. If I ask after her health, her reply makes my enquiry seem impertinent. If she comes into a classroom and finds the children laughing, she asks whether they are behaving properly, implying that I am not keeping order as I should. When I talk she makes me seem garrulous and when I am silent I seem to give the impression that I am sulking.

In spite of all this, I enjoy my visits to St Joseph's. I am left to conduct my work pretty much as I like. My solitary meals are restful. The children are eager and hardworking and, now they are no longer as painfully proper as they were when I started, really enjoy themselves.

Yes, they enjoy themselves all right and I think they have learnt quite a bit. Until this afternoon, I believed they would know better than to put on such a shoddy, under-rehearsed performance. I wouldn't have minded the rubbish quite so much if it had been well presented.

It was foolish of me to suppose those children would be as discriminating and responsible when they were on their own as when they were supervised. Well, from now on, I shall plan my teaching very differently.

Am I downhearted? YES.

EVENING CLASSES – 1

DURING the winter months I teach at the Braithwaite Settlement. This is a Quaker foundation offering evening classes for adults in a wide variety of subjects: mathematics, languages, literature, music, handicrafts and probably others, for all I know.

I used to think a settlement was a charitable institution set in a poor urban district, funded and patronised by various philanthropic bodies such as churches and public schools, for the benefit of local poor communities. Braithwaite isn't a bit like that. It stands just off a street of prosperous-looking shops and attracts men and women of all ages and many nationalities, denominations, occupations, interests and levels of income. Because it caters for the poor as well as for the better-off, fees for tuition are low as, unfortunately, are fees for tutors. I believe a small grant is made by the Local Education Authority but I think Braithwaite's upkeep is mostly paid for by the Society of Friends.

The Warden, Mr Crawford, is a man I like and respect a great deal. He runs the place single-handed, with the help of a few voluntary workers who clean it and provide the coffee bar. He is middle-aged, uneffusively friendly and almost inconspicuous, but he generates an atmosphere of cheerful activity and seems to know exactly what is going on – where, when and with whom. He believes that the acquisition of knowledge, the development of interests and skills should be available to everyone and for all sorts of reasons. So the ambitious, the studious, the lonely, the bored, the gregarious, the inquisitive, all come to Braithwaite at the end of their day, for refreshment, stimulus or simply for relaxation. The classes may or may not lead to higher qualifications or better pay but they give a lot of civilised pleasure.

I started teaching here last year, with a class in Speech Training. This year I am running another, followed by one in Public Speaking. Knowing nothing whatever about the second of these subjects, I have to spend hours in the public library, mugging up as much as I can about it and otherwise relying on my scant experience as both speaker and listener to carry me through. Mr Crawford took it for granted that I could cope and I was determined not to disappoint him, the students or myself.

This evening I am faced with a large beginners' class in Speech Training and spend the time finding out who everybody is and what each one hopes to achieve. I dread this proceeding. Some people enrol because of a speech defect, some are foreigners with unpronounceable names, some are so shy they can't bring themselves to speak above a whisper. All are ready to vanish after the first lesson, never to return, if they are bored or frightened, if the course doesn't seem to promise what they hoped from it or if they just don't like my face. There is nothing much I can do with my face except to wreathe it in smiles.

Beaming winningly at the rows of expressionless dials before me, I hear myself barking heartily and ingratiatingly into the silence. Trite, sweet phrases flow forth while I, inwardly cringing, listen to them with horror. My speech should set an example of perfect English, perfectly delivered, but I find myself either shouting or croaking, over-enunciating or perpetrating the most elementary grammatical errors.

This first class is even more mixed than last year's. There is a huge young man who tells me he is a policeman and finds it difficult to make himself heard in Court. There is a slightly adenoidal girl who is a cookery demonstrator for the Gas Board in a noisy departmental store, who has the same trouble. There is an earnest German woman who, after fifteen years in this country, has decided to try and improve her accent which is still so heavily Teutonic as to sound like a parody. There is a Polish girl who speaks very little English, a genteel lady of uncertain age who is keen on verse-speaking, an elderly lay-preacher, two little old women who run a sweet shop and like to have something to do of an evening (last year they did Cookery), a formidable Jewish corsetière, a lad from a school dramatic society, and his girl, a middle-aged black lady who can't be persuaded to utter, and one of my last-year students.

As my enquiries turn the anonymous mob into individuals, my smile grows ever brighter and more encouraging, while my spirits sink lower and lower. This gloom descended on me at the beginning of last year's course, but somehow I managed to interest at least some of the students for some of the time so I just hope I can do something for this lot.

I write down all the names, with a brief description beside each one, as a reminder. While I do this, most of the students sit silent and expectant, though I am pleased to hear a little whispered conversation here and there. So long as someone is talking, they may not notice how the minutes are slipping away.

When the list is complete, I can delay action no longer. I put down my pen, look up with the most brilliant smile yet, say "Well now!" loudly and purposefully, and embark on my opening words about Spoken English. As I speak, I notice the people who respond sympathetically, those who listen with suspicion and those who show not the slightest gleam of interest. At least I am sure they are all listening.

Now I get each student to read a few sentences aloud. This is not a complete success, for the Polish girl can barely read English, the Nigerian dissolves into helpless giggles, the lay-preacher – Mr Westcott – reels off his piece with the speed of a football commentator and the articulation of a fog-horn, and Miss Biggs, the verse-speaker, renders a few sentences of plain prose in the manner of a 19th century tragic actress. However, we are well away and, when everyone has had a turn, I am quite surprised to find it is time for the class to end. Some of the students rush away with obvious relief, while others stand about talking together. Two or three people wait to have a word with me. Mrs Cross, the German lady, is the first to approach. She smiles charmingly.

"I em so happy we hev soch a class. I hev lived here fifteen years and I still hev a Cherman accent. I should so like to speak gut. Ken I lurn, even so owld as I em?"

I make some guardedly encouraging remarks.

"I vill vurk. Yes. So. Cheerio."

Mr Westcott comes next. He is a small, birdlike man with a hybrid accent which I judge to belong somewhere in the West Country, though it is difficult to be sure of this for he talks very fast and in a low roar almost innocent of consonants except for an indiscriminate sprinkling of aitches. He is brisk and eager.

"Hi 'ow i's a bi' la' ter star' ha' moi hage. Se'n'y, Hi am – se'n'y lash mon'. Bu' Hi du a lo' o' preashin' an' some'imes Hi bin tol' they caan' yer ha the baa' o' the chapel. So Hi though' Hi'd ev a troy ha' thish yer helocootion. Never tu la' ter lear', hey?"

I assure Mr Westcott I will do all I can to help him.

"Hi don' min' bein' tol' moi mishtakes. Hanythin' Hi don' du ri', yu dell me. 'As wo' Hi come foor."

54

He smiles, bows, throws his mackintosh over his shoulder and strides away.

Now there is Miss Biggs, undulating up to me and with great, burning eyes. She tells me how experienced she is, how much she knows about verse-speaking, what successes she has had at competitive festivals and how she will go anywhere, but *anywhere* (with a look of mingled desperation and scorn towards the empty chairs that have so lately borne the ill-educated and Philistine students with whom she has forced herself to mix) for the 'sheer joy' of hearing and speaking poetry. She wouldn't get much out of this course, and so I tell her gently but frankly.

As a rule I have a twenty-minute break between classes. The interviews have reduced this to ten, but I think I may still have time for some coffee, so I hurry next door to the coffee-bar. Luckily, Mrs Brinkworth, one of my last-year students, has kept a chair for me and collected coffee and biscuits for the two of us. At the next table, a crowd of earnest students are gabbling away in Esperanto. Mrs Brinkworth beams through her glasses. She has a face like a tired, gentle horse.

"I half thought of deserting you this term and joining Beginners' German," she says, "but then I decided to have a go at your Public Speaking class. And now I'm scared stiff. If it wasn't for what Bert would say to me if I funked it, I believe I'd go straight home, but he'd be furious if I did."

Mrs Brinkworth seldom speaks for more than thirty seconds without mentioning either Bert or Meg, her husband and daughter. Mr Brinkworth is dying of an incurable disease and has recently become bedridden. He insists that his wife has one evening out a week, "to stretch my mind and see new faces", so she comes to the Braithwaite. Meg generally stays with him while her mother is out, though Mrs Brinkworth tries to get her brother-in-law to go in whenever he can. "Meg's a bit young for the responsibility," she explains.

Meg is fourteen and doing well at school. They hope to get her to University. She and her mother know that Mr Brinkworth won't last long and they are determined to face up to the fact and to accept it as cheerfully as he does himself. Apparently, when the diagnosis was confirmed, he said to them, "Now look here, you two, let's have no fuss about this, either now or when I'm gone. I shan't be perched on a cloud, playing a ruddy harp. I shall be finished, see? I'm afraid I've got to be a bit of a nuisance till it's all over but, once I'm dead, you go ahead and enjoy life. Mark my words, it's the only one you'll have so you'd better make the most of it."

"And then," went on Mrs Brinkworth, "he sent young Meg off to make the cocoa because he thought I might be silly enough to cry."

We go back to the classroom for the Public Speaking class. There are rows of empty chairs and a few people sitting at the back. Unless more students enrol within the next three weeks, the class will be closed. I go to the tutor's desk and start taking down names. Mrs Brinkworth sits alone in the front row, looking suitably serious.

There is a Mr Chadwick, a belligerent-looking man of about thirty-five, with a thin black moustache and horn-rimmed glasses, and a shy young couple, Mr and Mrs Wilkins. Miss Vandersteen is a youngish Dutch woman and Mr Dill is a stout gentleman in his fifties.

As I start my introductory remarks, the door bursts open and Mr Westcott appears. He strides up to my desk.

"Hi su'nly though' Hi migh' as well come to this class tu – hif you don' min'?"

I assure him he is welcome and he goes to sit beside Mrs Brinkworth. They smile at each other. I go on with what I had been saying and presently a tall, fair-haired man in his forties stands in the doorway, looking slightly bewildered. I ask him to come in and he strolls up to me, taking his time about it. As he speaks, an almost visible gust of whisky hits me in the face.

"I say," he says, "d'you mind if I join this class? My name's Trench-Stoddard. Sorry I'm a bit late. 'Fraid I was detained. The fact is, I have to do a certain amount of speechifying at the odd dinner and I get so damn nervous I can hardly get a word out. Can't enjoy the dinners either. I thought, if I bashed away here for a bit, I might get over it. What d'you think?"

I tell him that practice may very well help. Casting a nervous glance at the other students, he finds himself a chair as far away from them as possible. If the whisky was intended to give him Dutch courage, it has clearly not done its job.

I talk for a bit about speeches, their preparation and construction, promise work on breathing, relaxation (one eye on Mr Trench-Stoddard) and enunciation (one eye on Mr Westcott) and set the class a subject on which each one is to speak next week. Then, as there seems to be nothing else I can do with them for the rest of the lesson, I suggest they try some extempore speeches, thereby contradicting the principles about preparation I have just laid down. I ask each one to introduce a speaker and to tell the audience a little about him or her.

"Not more than two minutes," I tell them, "and one minute would be better."

Mr Westcott glances at the others who are all studying their shoes with close attention. He stands up. "Hi don' min'," he says. I invite him up to the tutor's desk and seat myself amongst the audience.

Mr Westcott strikes a Napoleonic attitude, clears his throat and lets out a sustained roar. I try to make out what he is saying. I tell myself to concentrate and only succeed in concentrating on concentrating. Every now and then a word emerges from the general noise

57

but it's impossible to connect it with any particular theme.

After about three minutes of this performance, I take a deep breath and shout, "Mr Westcott!" It is a waste of effort. The voice booms on. I stand up and wave my notebook in the air to attract his attention. He smiles broadly and stops in mid-bellow. A blessed silence falls on us for a moment.

"I'm sorry to interrupt you, Mr Westcott," I say (and, compared to his, my voice sounds like that of a half-strangled kitten) "But I'm afraid you have exceeded your two minutes. I won't make any comments now. We'll hear the others first."

I pray some suitable comments will occur to me within the next few minutes – critical but encouraging – and, meanwhile, in case the emboldening but waning effects of the whisky wear off altogether, I get the late-comer, Mr Trench-Stoddard, to speak next. As he goes to the front of the class, he looks slightly dazed, though whether from Mr Westcott's battering, his own nervousness or the drink it's impossible to tell. He coughs, clasps his hands and, with an expression of utter misery, says, "Ladies and gentlemen – ah – it gives me much pleasure – ah – " He opens his mouth but utters not another word. He looks down at the desk and then up at the ceiling. "It gives me very much pleasure . . ." he says again, loudly, stops and bites his lip. I make encouraging noises. At the next attempt he succeeds in introducing "Sir Donald Bradman, the famous Australian cricketer," before I let him off and he goes thankfully back to his seat.

Mrs Brinkworth is next. She clutches the desk as though it was the only solid object between her and a fifty-foot drop, assumes a sickly smile, manages to string three sentences together, giggles, says "Well, that's all I've got to say, so without more ado, let's give a hearty welcome to our distinguished speaker," and rushes back to her seat with the alacrity of one playing musical chairs.

Throughout these proceedings Mr and Mrs Wilkins sit without stirring, and Mr Dill has been making copious notes in an exercise book. Mr Chadwick lounges in his chair, one arm thrown over the back and a supercilious smirk on his face. I don't at all like the look of him and decide not to call him until everyone else has had a turn.

Mrs Wilkins stands at attention at the desk. She says her piece swiftly and neatly, like a schoolgirl calling for three cheers at the end of a prize-giving day. Her husband stumbles and stutters a bit but keeps going until he has said his say. Miss Vandersteen, the only foreigner in the room, introduces her speaker fluently and graciously in a low, pleasant voice with hardly a trace of a Dutch accent. There is a burst of spontaneous applause and even Mr Chadwick is surprised into looking less condescending.

I can put him off no longer.

When I call his name, he walks briskly to the front of the class, clasps his lapels and lets fly in a voice loud and harsh enough to slice through a piece of sheet-metal at twenty paces.

"Comrades," he shouts, "I'm proud to introduce Comrade Herbert Rendell, a Man of the People, who devotes his life to helping the downtrodden working classes. Some of us are sick and tired of the way this country is run by well-housed, well-dressed, well-fed nincompoops who don't give a thought to the slum dweller trying to support a wife and family on a mere pittance – if he's lucky enough to have even that. Now, Herbert Rendell has just spent a month in Russia, long enough to see how a country *can* be run when the right people are in charge; when working people unite to fight for their rights."

Oh dear, oh dear. Mr Chadwick shouts on and I only half listen, for I'm wondering how this speech is being

. . . sick and tired of the way this country is run

received by the 'nincompoops' here assembled. I sit with my back to them, so I can't see their faces. Of course I should have stipulated no politics or religion but it never occurred to me. At last Mr Chadwick bellows, "Herbert Rendell!", gives me a triumphant grin and strides back to his seat. As I move up to the desk, Mr Trench-Stoddard says, "I say!", laughs aloud and claps his hands twice, very slowly. The others gratefully follow his lead and laugh as though Mr Chadwick had been merely a comic turn. Apart from the glowering Chadwick, the only unsmiling one is Mr Westcott who, red in the face, bursts out with "We don' wan' no Russian ways 'ere. I 'ope we know better. This is a Chris'ian coun'ry. Rich an' poor ali', we're all i' the 'and o' Go' an' 'E 'as 'is own purposes for each one of us."

Mr Chadwick laughs scornfully and mirthlessly.

"Strikes me," says Mr Wilkins, "the gentleman hasn't left much for the speaker to say. He's said it already."

"Best leave religion and politics out of it," says Mr Dill.

I agree with both these last remarks, and say so, adding a bit about winning the sympathy of an audience and suiting volume of voice to the size of the hall. Then I swiftly dole out sugar-coated pills of criticism to the other speakers and bring the class to an end.

"It's going to be a lively course and no mistake," says Mrs Brinkworth, as she leaves me in the entrance hall. "My word! I'll have a lot to tell Bert!"

ST MARK'S CHURCH

ONE evening a week, when I get home from my day's teaching, I just have time to swallow a sandwich and some coffee before setting off for St Mark's Church. This is an ugly, late Victorian church in a suburb of dreary but respectable terraced houses, and I'm to produce a play here with some of the parishioners.

I must be mad to take on more work when it's hard enough to manage the preparation, travelling and teaching I already do, but it's ages since I actually staged a play and I long to get back to some kind of production.

I said as much to Miss Simpson when we met for tea at Lyons Corner House during the holidays. She is a retired Elementary School headmistress who was kind and helpful when, as a student, I struggled through teaching practice at her school. We rather took to each other and still meet from time to time.

She suggested I approach a Mr Harrington, one of the Local Education Officers whose job it is to appoint Adult Education tutors.

"I've known him since he was a young man," she said, "You can quote my name if you like; it just might help. I've tried for years to get him to take an interest in drama and he seems to agree with all I say about it when I'm with him and then, when I've gone, does nothing about it. Play up the educational and social value of drama for all you're worth.''

She also told me of an Adult Education tutor she knows, who is supposed to be running a course in dramatic literature, with the students seated at desks, reading Shakespeare. Instead, he gets them out on the floor, acting, and has even put on a public performance in a local school hall. So far, apparently, his employers have not objected. She thinks I might be able to do the same sort of thing.

I thanked Miss Simpson for her advice and promised to let her know how I got on with Mr Harrington.

MR Harrington's office is tiny and almost filled by a huge desk bearing 'in' and 'out' trays and masses of files and loose papers. There is just room for his chair on one side of the desk and mine on the other. He is a mild, colourless man who looks rather bored but not bored enough to be rude. When I say my piece about Miss Simpson he brightens up considerably.

''A wonderful old lady,'' he says. I fervently agree.

As luck would have it, he has recently had a letter from the Vicar of St Mark's Church, asking if he can supply someone to produce a Christmas play with members of the congregation and explaining why such a collaborative enterprise would be socially and educationally desirable for the parish as a whole as well as for the participants. After a prolonged scuffle through the papers on his desk, Mr Harrington finds the letter and reads it to me.

''To be honest with you, Miss – er – Garth,'' he says, ''I can't see why the Vicar or someone in the congregation can't produce a play. There is surely no need for a tutor.''

''Perhaps,'' I suggest, in deceptively mild tones, ''he needs someone who knows something about play production. It is, you know, a specialised job."

"I suppose you are trained in this sort of thing?" he asks, slightly amused.

I assure him I am well trained and experienced. Do I sound more like a children's nanny or a sheepdog?

There is a pause while he considers what next to ask me. Should I extol the benefits of amateur drama (as Miss Simpson advised), blow my own trumpet or hold my tongue? Then he asks, "Can you name three of Galsworthy's plays?"

I am taken aback by this apparently irrelevant question and it takes me a few seconds to answer. Then, "*Strife*, *The Silver Box* and *Justice*," I say in a rush. He nods and smiles, though whether because I am able to answer or because he admires Galsworthy I can't tell. There is another pause.

"Oh, very well," he says at last. "Of course you realise, Miss – er – Bath, it will be only a temporary appointment – just till Christmas."

So I've got the job (thanks, it seems, to John Galsworthy) and, though the pay barely covers my expenses, never mind. Every little helps and anyway I need the experience.

MR Stevens, the young Vicar, has an air of childlike innocence which I find very appealing. He is small, agile and neat, with fair hair and wide blue eyes, and he bounds about, smiling and laughing.

Mrs Stevens is tall, slim, spectacled and without humour. I am sure she is always kind, with a kindness emanating from 'Christian duty' rather than from any natural warmth of heart. She is a little older than her husband and looks tired. No doubt they work unceasingly for their flock and, I should say, for a meagre stipend. They look to me to be pretty hard up.

Our first meeting is in the vicarage dining-room. The vicarage is the biggest house in the district and even uglier than the church next door to it. Mrs Stevens brings her husband and me a cup of tea each and then leaves us. Mr Stevens talks a bit about the parish and about his idea of putting on a Christmas play.

"We're all getting a bit stodgy," he tells me. "I felt we needed some communal activity to wake us up and draw us together, and a new way to celebrate Christmas, apart from the usual carol service. I'm afraid we aren't the easiest lot of people to deal with (lots of silly feuds and that sort of thing) but I'm sure you, coming from outside the parish, will be able to get everyone working happily together. I'm so glad you've come to help."

I begin to feel extremely uneasy.

Presently Mrs Stevens joins us and we walk across to the church, where we are to meet those of the congregation who want to take part in the play and where rehearsals and performance are to be held, there being no church hall.

The empty church is dim and cold. Mr Stevens hurries to switch on a few lights and sets chairs for himself and me just below the chancel steps, facing the nave. Mrs Stevens goes to sit in one of the front pews.

People start to come in by the north door. Women. All women. Old ones, middle-aged ones, young ones, of all shapes and sizes. Not one man. They come in pairs, in trios or singly, and Mr Stevens bounds over to greet each of them and settle them in the front pews where they talk in low voices to one another, casting wary glances in my direction. When about fifteen are assembled, he introduces me, telling them how lucky they are to have a professional producer to help them and what fun it will be to put on their first Christmas play. Two or three look pleased and hopeful. The rest just stare.

"And now, without more ado . . ." says Mr Stevens, sits beside me and off I go on my ice-breaking gambit,

65

very bright and feeling sick with nerves. Then, "Why are there no men?" I ask.

They look surprised and one of them says, "Oh, well, the men wouldn't want to do play-acting," and they all laugh at the very idea.

None of them has done any play-acting since leaving school and some, not even then. Few have ever been to a theatre, not even to the pantomime. I wonder how the Vicar persuaded them to attempt a play.

A week later. Today we meet in the church. Having to audition everyone, I try to keep the whole thing light-hearted and jolly as I give them pieces to read and things to do. One of the few personable young women has a cleft palate and can't speak comprehensibly. Several of the older ones can hardly read, can't tell left from right, can't walk faster than pall-bearers, can't understand the simplest directions and, when required to exercise some imagination, look at me blankly or dissolve into giggles. Luckily I spy three or four who are alert, intelligent and interested but even they (including Mrs Stevens) have no idea how to turn the printed word into convincing speech.

After this meeting I suggest to Mr Stevens that it might be wise to hold a few classes in speech and movement before attempting a play.

"Oh, no," he says, amused at such a notion. "They don't want to learn about acting. They just want to put on a play."

So now I'm adapting a mimed nativity play devised years ago by a friend of mine and which I produced with my fellow students during my training. At least the group will have only to learn something about movement and need not struggle with speech and the learning of lines.

I sit up till after midnight, planning and casting.

SEVERAL weeks later.

We rehearse for two hours once a week, so much of what has been achieved one week is forgotten by the next. There are a few stalwarts who turn up regularly and on time, two or three habitual late-comers, and Mrs Pring, a dangerous gossip and trouble-maker.

She draws me aside before one of the rehearsals.

"You know that Marlene Green," she says in a hoarse whisper. "She said she couldn't come to rehearsal last week because her mother was poorly. Well, I saw her out walking with that young Rudge boy when I was on my way here."

I had cast Mrs Pring as one of the householders who wouldn't give shelter to the Holy Family on Christmas Eve. Now she tells me she can't and won't play the part.

"It's just not in my nature," she says, "to be so unkind."

So I've given the part to someone else who is enjoying it and doing it quite well. Mrs Pring is one of the crowd in the street and she stands about glowering and sighing, burning with jealousy.

Mrs Riddle is to play Mary. She is rather too old for the part but she has imagination, understands what it's about and is beginning to mime quite convincingly. Joseph is a large, stolid woman with enough sense to do what is required of her and to stand about looking worried, sympathetic or reverent, according to the state of play. Mrs Stevens plays the Angel Gabriel reliably and with dignity. ("Of course you'd have to give her that part," mutters Mrs Pring, "she being the Vicar's wife." Surely that old witch didn't think she herself could play it?) For the rest, Innkeeper, Wise Men, Shepherds, Angels – they are beginning to accommodate themselves to my curious demands and to enjoy themselves. But we have a long way to go before we are ready for any kind of performance.

. . . not in my nature to be so unkind

AFTER our first meeting, when I had decided on the play, I handed Mr Stevens the book of old French carols which are to accompany the mimes. He was able to recruit a few singers from his church choir and, having made copies of both words and music, undertook to coach them. The organist can't or won't help, so the Vicar plays for them, with gusto and a fair sprinkling of wrong notes. Mrs Stevens offered to type the words of all the carols for the players and I have exhorted them to memorise these so that their actions really fit, even though they themselves won't be singing. At rehearsals, Mr Stevens bangs away on a tinny old piano (we shall have the organ for the performance) and he and I bellow the carols at the top of our voices, to keep the action going.

We shall have to build up a bit of a stage between nave and chancel, or only people in the front pews will see anything. But what to build with? I ask the cast for suggestions. Caspar's husband is a carpenter and joiner and can probably supply a strong crate or two. Mary's father-in-law is a publican and can certainly lend some wooden beer crates.

"Beer crates in *church*!" exclaims Melchior, scandalised.

"We should be grateful for any offering," says Mr Stevens. When they are called an offering, beer crates seem quite respectable. Melchior says no more.

SOME time ago I devised a simple little dance for three angels to perform, in celebration of Christ's birth. The young dancers did it quite well for a couple of weeks and then one of them started to dance with all the grace and verve of a hippopotomus. Questions, exhortations, encouragement, threats – all had no effect. The girl went on galumphing about, looking sulky, much to the annoyance of the other two.

"What on earth's the matter with Doris?" I ask Mr Stevens this evening.

"I'm afraid we're having a bit of an up-and-a-downer there," he tells me. "Doris has decided she doesn't approve of dancing in church."

"Well, why doesn't she *tell* me so?" I ask. "She can drop out of the dance and we'll just have the other two."

"She wants to be in the play."

"Do you mean to tell me she thinks it more reverent to dance badly than to dance as well as she knows how?"

"That's about the size of it. A bit of an up-and-a-downer, isn't it?"

"Vicar, this is your department," I say. "Tell her about David dancing before the Ark. Tell her she either dances her best or not at all and, even if she thinks acting, as opposed to dancing, is all right in church, there is no other part for her in the play."

My estimation of the Vicar's influence over his flock has risen considerably, for this evening, after he had had a few words with her in private, Doris is dancing like a true and happy angel and I anticipate no more trouble with her.

FROM somewhere or other Mr and Mrs Stevens have heard about the forthcoming London Religious Drama Festival, a competition open to local amateur players. They want our lot to take part. I am sure we are not anything like good enough, but the Festival is not to be held till after Christmas by which time we shall have given our church performance, so there is time to improve. The Stevenses will be deeply disappointed if I refuse to enter.

In the end I relent, partly because the thought of a competition will spur everybody on like anything and, still more, because I hear the adjudicator is to be a distinguished actor/producer who is much involved with religious drama and particularly interested in unusual forms of production. Well, our mimed play is both religious and unusual, if nothing else.

If I ever thought I could produce this play after only

a few weekly rehearsals of two hours a time, I was much mistaken. I have had to get over to St Mark's on several extra evenings, after my day's work, to consult Caspar's husband about platforms and steps, and Mary's father-in-law about beer crates, measure up these units and, once home again, make a scale plan of the stage they are to construct. Both men are nice, helpful chaps and they have offered to round up a few pals, bring the stuff to the church and instal it. We shall need at least two rehearsals on this new stage, and so I tell Mr Stevens. He looks embarrassed.

"I'm afraid we've got a bit of an up-and-a-downer here," he says. "You see, we simply can't have all that staging there during services."

"Not even for dress rehearsals?"

"Afraid not," he says, pink in the face but quite firm. Of course he's right. I tend to forget what a church is actually *for*.

I appoint Caspar as Stage Manager, tell her what has to be done and we all (including the Vicar who takes off his jacket and heaves away with the rest of us) drag the bits of staging to a dark corner of the south aisle after each rehearsal. All, that is, except Mrs Pring who says, "It's my back, Miss Garth" and sits peacefully watching our struggles. I worry about Mrs Stevens who works as hard as any of us and is clearly not up to all that heavy heaving.

Caspar turns out to be reliable and efficient. She now has a copy of the stage plan and sees to it that her husband and the other men build up the units correctly before our two meagre dress-rehearsals, even though we have to dismantle them afterwards. They will see that all is ready and in place for the performance.

REUBEN, one of the Shepherds, works in a draper's shop and says she can probably get a few lengths of calico, Bolton sheeting and mutton-cloth cheap, for some of the costumes. She and her mum will make a few, some of the cast will make their own and others will bring curtains and bits of material for the more skilled women to adapt and make up into garments. I've shown them pictures so that they can see the kind of shapes and colours we need. In spite of this, Melchior presents me with a Victorian evening dress in mauve taffeta which belonged to her 'lady' when she was in service, and Doris (the Third Angel who was so tiresome about the dance) offers a faded pink velveteen jacket and her late grandmother's tattered fur coat. It is difficult not to hurt people's feelings when they eagerly contribute such unsuitable things.

Now that it comes to dressing up, everyone is agog with excitement.

WE have had two dress rehearsals. At the first one the singers were drowned by Mr Stevens' exuberant organ-playing (though he now plays the right notes), one of the Shepherds tripped over a step and twisted her ankle quite badly, and Joseph came on in court shoes instead of sandals. At the second one there were no accidents but the play was about as lively as a suet pudding. The cast are well aware of this, but they are tired. Perhaps I have overworked them.

NOW it's the night of the performance. The cast are dressing in the crypt, with a small paraffin stove to fend off the worst of the cold. They are all excited, nervous, talkative, and I move among them, begging them to calm down, think what they have to do, and be quiet. I am as nervous as any of them but try to emanate calm confidence. I can hear Mr Stevens playing an unsuitable but heartening organ voluntary. Having dissuaded the Angels from piling on lipstick, I hand over to Caspar who, as Stage Manager, is now in charge, wish everybody

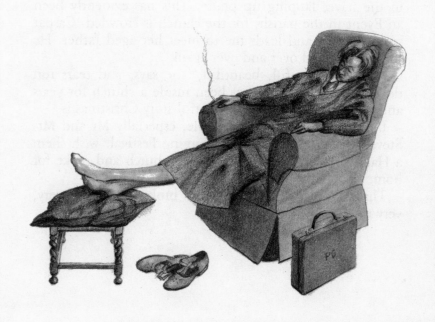

I am very, very tired

luck and go to find a pew at the back of the church. Now it's up to them.

IT'S over. I'm amazed that it went as well as it did. Of course it was a bit rough and unready, but it worked. Everyone remembered what had to be done and put her heart into it. Perhaps the fact that they are all members of the church congregation helped.

Now the performers mingle with friends and relations in the nave, lapping up praise. This has evidently been an Event in the parish, for the church is crowded. Caspar seeks me out and leads me to meet her aged father. He shakes my hand over and over again.

"It was beautiful, beautiful," he says, and tears run down his cheek. "I've not been inside a church for years and I'd forgotten what a wonderful story Christmas is."

I say goodbye to a few people, especially Mr and Mrs Stevens, remind them of the coming Festival, wish them a Happy Christmas, slip out of the church and make for home.

Thank heaven the schools have broken up. I am very, very tired.

THE LONDON RELIGIOUS
DRAMA FESTIVAL

THE Drama Festival is to be held in a little theatre in the City. I go there one morning and seek out the lame old caretaker who is, at first, surly and uncooperative but who gradually thaws and becomes quite pleasant and talkative as he shows me round, telling me about his gammy leg and about the mess the dressing-rooms were left in after the last show. Trying to be sympathetic and observant at the same time, I see that there's a decent-sized stage with grey drapes, adequate lighting, hardly any wing-space and what there is, occupied by an upright piano which will have to be lowered into the auditorium where there is just enough room for it and the singers in a corner below the stage.

We descend to the dressing-rooms – two of them – each with a few hooks and rails, blotched mirrors barely lit by low-wattage bulbs, and some chairs. Then we go under the stage where, to my delight, I find steps and rostra which we may be able to use instead of the crates and beer-crates we had at St Mark's. I out with my tape-measure and surreptitiously mark those that would build into the many-levelled staging we need.

Next day I go and see Mr and Mrs Stevens. I tell them we need several strong men to lift the piano from the wings onto the floor of the auditorium and some platforms and steps from under the stage, and that everything will have to be put back in its place before we leave the theatre.

"Leave it to us," says Mrs Stevens, "People have been so thrilled with the play that I don't think it will be difficult to recruit a few men."

Mr Stevens is as excited as a small boy with a new train-set.

"I've booked a bus to take us all to the theatre and back," he tells me. "I hope everyone will contribute to the cost. Anyway, blow the expense!"

I'm excited too, but my head aches and I feel rather ill. Am I sickening for something? I simply must keep going. I manage to make a list of things to be taken to the theatre such as towels and soap and thermos flasks of tea and . . . and . . . It's no good, I've got to get home and to bed. The Stevenses are solicitous. He summons a taxi. Again, blow the expense!

I feel terrible. I spent yesterday in bed and so missed the first day of the Festival. Three plays were to be performed and I should have been there to see them. Did any of our lot go, I wonder? I urged them to do so. They would have enjoyed it and might have learnt a thing or two.

My head aches and I keep sweating and shivering by turns. I simply must get up soon. Not yet though. Not yet.

Have they got the steps up from the basement and stacked in the wings, ready to set on stage? Have they lifted the piano down to the floor of the hall? Will everyone turn up on time?

'Don't worry so,' I keep telling myself. 'Your job is done. It's up to them now. You're not indispensable.' But I really think that's just what I am, so I keep on worrying.

The door-bell rings. I struggle out of bed and go to peer over the half-door. Mrs Stevens stands in the mews. I pull on my dressing-gown and go down to let her in. She gives me one look, enters briskly in her role of Vicar's Wife Visiting the Sick, orders me back to bed, refills my hot-water bottle, goes to the kitchen to make tea, assures me that everything at St Mark's is under control and that she, the Vicar, Caspar and two able-bodied men went to the theatre early this morning and dealt with the steps and the piano and will cope with everything this evening. She tells me I must on no account leave my bed but I insist that, even if I miss the other productions, I simply must see ours and, over-riding her protests, get her to promise she will order a taxi to get me to the theatre in time. (I just hope I have enough money to pay for it). Then that kind, sensible woman leaves me and I crawl back into bed, set the alarum and, when it rings, get up and wash and dress slowly and carefully.

The taxi arrives punctually and drops me at the stage door. From the passage inside I hear a sonorous male voice booming away on the stage. I creep along to the dressing-rooms and find all our women squashed into the first one in various states of undress and chattering away like starlings while Mrs Stevens and Caspar make still more noise hushing them.

There is distant applause signalling the end of the play before ours. When it's over, I start to climb up to the stage and then retreat as two youths and a desperate-looking old woman lug a table, some chairs and various props into the wings where everyone is likely to fall over them. I suggest to the woman (obviously the producer) that everything should be stacked elsewhere (I feel much better now there's a job to do) and she says, "Oh, Lord! Must we? Oh, all right. Cecil! Take the chairs downstairs and put the table and props behind the back drapes." I thank her and she gives me a tired smile. "What hell it all is,'' she says. ''Why on earth do we bother?'' I tell her it's because we can't be quite right in the head and then I retreat while Cecil and his mate do her bidding.

We are allowed twenty minutes between plays.

Mr Stevens, two men I don't know, and Caspar, bring on and build up platforms and steps according to my plan and I check to make sure they are safe. Members of the cast wander on, get in the way and have to be chivvied off. Doris peers through the curtain to see whether her mum is in the audience. I shout at her and she retires, deeply offended.

The adjudicator pings his bell. Mr Stevens, the singers and I hurry through the pass-door and gather round the piano. I would rather be at the back of the hall but there's no time to get there. I can see the adjudicator sitting at a dimly lit table. I get another attack of the shivers and aches though I can't tell whether they are due to 'flu or nerves. Probably both and I hope I'm not infecting everybody. Too late to think of that now.

Mr Stevens starts the first carol. The curtain rises. When I look at the stage I feel sick and dizzy, so I shut my eyes and imagine the production as I first saw it in my mind's eye. I fall asleep.

IT'S all over bar the adjudication. The adjudicator mounts the stage, holding his notes. We applaud him. He is a tall, dark man with a mellifluous voice. I'm sure his criticism of the first play is helpful but I don't take in a word.

Then it comes to the St Mark's Players in *Thy Light is Come*. I whisper to the Vicar, ''Try and take down what he says,'' and Mr Stevens dives into his pocket, pulls out a notebook and pencil and scribbles away at top speed. Try as I will, I simply can't keep awake.

I'm awakened by a burst of applause and by Mr Stevens shaking my arm.

"Go on, Miss Garth. We've won. Go and receive the award."

"Oh no," I protest. "You go." But he insists and I have to obey. I waver up to the stage and find myself confronted, not by the adjudicator, but by the well-known critic of a national newspaper, a stout, grey-haired man who hands me a small, silver cup. Through the applause I hear him say, "You know, I really can't stand that sort of thing, but congratulations anyway."

I do not repeat this remark to the ecstatic cast and singers, not even to Mr and Mrs Stevens to whom I hand over the cup.

"My hubby's got his van here," says Caspar. "We'll take you home if you like."

"Steps to the basement, dressing-rooms left tidy, piano in the wings," I mutter.

"All done," says Mr Stevens. "You go home to bed."

I go down to the dressing-room, congratulate everybody again and wish them a Happy New Year.

"Happy New Year," they say in chorus, all smiling – even Mrs Pring – and Mrs Stevens and Caspar lead me to the van very tenderly.

And so to bed.

INTERLUDE

SOON after last half-term, on one of my visits to Fettington Court, Mrs Lumley-Stanford gave me the sack. That is to say, she told me she had decided to lay on a course of Modern Dance during the spring and summer terms but would be glad to have me back in the autumn. I don't suppose the Modern Dance teacher – whoever she is – will fancy this arrangement any more than I do and anyway it is usual to give a term's notice. I am not arguing about it for I'm determined never to darken the doors of Fettington Court again.

However, the drop in income is a blow. Mrs L-S paid well, when she remembered to give me my cheque. It never seemed to occur to her that I needed the money to live on and when, weeks late, she handed me the longed-for plain envelope, it was with the air of someone offering a lollipop to a child, knowing it would harm its teeth.

When I went to say goodbye, Mrs L-S lightly touched my hand with both of hers, looked at me deeply, slightly shook her head and said, "My dear Miss Garth, it's been such a . . . But we shall have you with us again after . . ." I smiled back with a look of mingled regret, understanding and respect and moved unhurriedly out of the drawing-room for the last time. No need, at the moment, to tell her I shall not be coming back.

DURING the Christmas holidays I bought a car. George, the driver of the Daimler which lives under my flat, told me of a Baby Austin for sale, belonging to a friend of his who owns a garage in the Portobello Road. So I went to have a look at it.

It's ten years old and looks its age, but it certainly has character. I bought it for £5 and George has arranged for me to garage it in the mews for 2/6d. a week. So now I'm free of those awful bus and train journeys and can drive to all my schools. I trundle along very happily except that, at this time of year, the little car is terribly cold and, however much I wrap up, I generally arrive half frozen. Still, my new independence is worth the agony.

HOLIDAY TIME – 1

AFTER that untimely bout of 'flu I feel that a breath of country air would do me good, and thanks to my new-found freedom I have invited myself to stay with Aunt Gwen and Uncle Bob. They live in Buckinghamshire halfway up a Chiltern hill, and as I pull up by their front door they both come out to greet me.

"How are you, niece?" asks Uncle Bob. "Pretty well?" This is always how he greeted me when I was a small girl and once or twice a term on a Sunday rescued me from my first boarding-school and carried me back on the pillion of his bicycle to a sumptuous tea. "Pretty well?" seemed a decently grown-up sort of query and I would try to respond in an equally grown-up manner, to which he would exclaim "Capital!" before I climbed up behind him, wrapped my arms round his waist and was pedalled back to Aunt Gwen, scones, strawberry jam, two kinds of cake and tea.

And now, "What fun!" says Aunt Gwen. "You couldn't have come at a better time. We're rehearsing our pantomime (it's *The Sleeping Beauty* this year) and I knew you'd be interested so I asked Colonel Rivers if I could bring you to this evening's rehearsal."

Is there no escape? I thought I was here on holiday, but I respond with a suitable show of enthusiasm.

After lunch Uncle Bob retires to his workshop in the garden, where he makes model steam-engines and boats and has made a gramophone and various ingenious machines of the Heath Robinson variety. Aunt Gwen settles down by the fire and starts sewing sham ermine onto the pantomime king's red robe. Having been assured that there is nothing I can do to help either of them, I take myself off for a walk up the garden, across the stile and along the familiar track to the woods. Here, remembering a childhood habit, I wade noisily through the fallen beech leaves, startling a bird into sudden flight up through the bare branches. These woods, and the solitude I enjoyed in them as a child, still confer a sort of blessing.

I do so wish I could live in the country. I hate London. Taking a deep breath, I shout at the top of my voice, "I HATE LONDON!" The shouting does me good and calms me down enough to remember that London is where I have to be, to earn a living in the only way I know. It's not a bad life, better than being stuck in an office all day or confined with others of my kind in some boarding-school as a resident schoolmistress. I like my job and believe in it, though few people seem to think it as important as I do.

I leave the woods, walk down across the fields and then turn up the drive to the house, feeling refreshed.

"We'll have an early tea," says Aunt Gwen. "Would you go and call Uncle Bob while I put on the kettle? I told Lily she could have the afternoon off to go and see her sister, but she's made a few scones and a Victoria sponge. She'll be back to get Uncle Bob his supper and I've asked her to leave something cold for us, for when we get home from the rehearsal."

Uncle Bob is busy painting the wooden sword he has

made for the principal boy, with a silver blade and a gold hilt.

"Must just finish this," he says. "Shan't be a moment. I'm afraid it won't be dry by this evening though. The prince will have to manage with a broomstick again."

During tea Aunt Gwen tells me we shall have to call at Lee Grange on our way to the village hall, to pick up Megan, the bad fairy, and an antique spinning-wheel.

"Lee Grange is where the Morgan-Vaughans live," she explains. "We call them The Three Weird Sisters and that's exactly what they are, though they're a good deal younger than how we imagine the Macbeth trio. Nobody seems to know why they left their native Wales to settle in a mouldering Tudor mansion in Bucks. They never ask anyone in and they never go out together, only seperately and very occasionally. Megan's the youngest and liveliest of the three and a talented actress, but although she must be in her twenties, she is completely dominated by the other two, especially by Nesta, the eldest and most witch-like. Megan has escaped, very occasionally, to take part in one of the Lee Dramatic Society productions but she's a bit of a liability because she doesn't drive, the Society rehearses some miles away, Nesta and Enid would never bother to take her there and anyway I'm sorry to say she drinks – I mean really *drinks.*"

Uncle Bob joins us. "Megan? She's tight most of the time, I believe," he says. "I can't think how the other two allow all that gin into the house."

I offer to go to fetch Megan and the spinning-wheel but they tell me my car is too small and anyway I would never find the way. Aunt Gwen will take their capacious Humber which, though quite as old as my little Austin, has been looked after by Uncle Bob with loving skill and looks half its age. Uncle Bob doesn't come to rehearsals.

Aunt Gwen has packed up a picnic basket with thermos

84

flasks, sandwiches and biscuits ("rehearsals do tend to drag on so") and off we go.

It is dusk when we arrive at Lee Grange. Aunt Gwen tugs at the iron bell-pull and presently the door is opened by a dark, wild-looking woman with a mass of dark hair. Even in the half-light I can see that she must be in her forties and must surely be Nesta, Witch No. 1.

"Please come in, Mrs Richards," she says in a cold but resonant Welsh voice. "I expect Megan is ready."

Aunt Gwen extracts me from the car and, having introduced me to Miss Morgan-Vaughan (who gives me a brief look but doesn't shake hands), we follow her in silence through a dark little ante-room into an equally dark hall or sitting-room where she switches on a single table-lamp. This, rather than providing light, throws huge shadows up to a ceiling so lofty as to be invisible, though it also falls on the lower steps of a wide and handsome staircase.

She doesn't invite us to sit down, so we stand about in the gloom as she goes to the foot of the stairs and calls up "Megan! Mrs Richards is here. Come along. Enid! Enid, bring down the spinning-wheel. Don't let Megan touch it and do be careful."

She is answered by a distant shout, presumably from one or other of the two witches.

"It's so good of you to lend it," says Aunt Gwen. "We'll take the greatest care of it."

"Yes, well, it *is* valuable. It belonged to our great-grandmother and I'm not too keen on letting it out of the house, but you can have it for this one production if you will look after it between rehearsals and performances. Don't let Megan touch it. She's so – unreliable."

We wait in silence and semi-darkness and presently Enid clumps down the uncarpeted stairs, carrying the spinning-wheel. She greets us briefly, sets it down and switches on a standard lamp which slightly relieves the

85

gloom. She is quite a good-looking woman, a good few years younger than her elder sister, with bobbed hair and, like Nesta, a pale, unsmiling face.

We are presently joined by the third and youngest Weird Sister. She creeps down the stairs on soft-soled shoes, clutching the banister with one hand, and carrying some black garment. She is wearing an old green tweed coat and a battered felt hat. When she moves into the light I see that she is beautiful (and 'beautiful' is not a word I remember using about anyone I have known,) with sad, dark eyes and fine, ivory features. She smiles vaguely in our direction but doesn't speak.

"You're keeping Mrs Richards waiting," says Nesta.

"No, no," Aunt Gwen assures her, "there's plenty of time."

Nesta grasps her arm, Enid picks up the spinning-wheel and we all move to the front door. As Nesta pushes her into the passenger seat beside Aunt Gwen, she says fiercely "Pull yourself together, Megan." I climb in at the back, with the spinning-wheel. Nesta and Enid go back into the house and shut the front door before Aunt Gwen has even started the car.

After a few moments Aunt Gwen tries to start a conversation but Megan barely responds. She sits slumped in her seat, occasionally humming to herself. So Aunt Gwen and I talk brightly to each other and I wonder how on earth Megan will ever be able to do any acting this evening.

The hall is much the same as other village halls. It's long and narrow, dimly lit by a few dangling bulbs with white shades. There is a black iron stove emitting a trickle of evil-smelling smoke and precious little warmth, and a lot of wooden chairs (designed to provide maximum discomfort), some of them against the wall and others dragged out for the use of actors not wanted on the stage.

The stage is about the size and shape of a large sideboard and so high that any actor moving to the front risks an attack of vertigo. On either side hang grubby green curtains, embellished with remnants of pink crêpe paper left over, I suppose, from the children's Christmas party.

Aunt Gwen has brought in the picnic basket, has seated Megan at the back of the hall and is plying her with black coffee.

Now she leads me to meet Colonel Rivers who greets me briefly but is clearly far too busy shouting to some invisible being tinkering with plugs on the switchboard to be bothered with an unnecessary young woman, though he admires the spinning-wheel clasped in my arms. Following Aunt Gwen, I climb the rickety steps up to the stage, descend still more rickety steps at the back and we find our way to a dressing-room where there is a cupboard in which the spinning-wheel may safely be stowed until it's wanted.

"Let's sit for a moment," says Aunt Gwen. "They won't be starting yet and I want to warn you about Colonel Rivers. I should really have told you about him before, but Uncle Bob so loathes him that I hardly dare mention his name at home."

"Why does Uncle Bob loathe him?" I ask.

"Well, he's often very rude to people and he is absolutely beastly to Rose, his wife. But he does produce lively and amusing pantomimes so the rest of us forgive him, especially because of his war-wound."

Colonel Rivers, she tells me, has been producing the annual pantomime for the past ten or twelve years. He writes much of it himself, chooses the songs, gathers the company together, rehearses them and always plays the Dame, with much comic business and ad-libbing that generally steals the show. He won't shave off his small, grey moustache, so he camouflages it with layers of grease-paint, and he always puts on an elaborate red or yellow wig.

He wears a metal plate over the hole in his head, held in place with black elastic. As a rule, he is brusque but good-humoured with his cast, knows exactly what he wants from them and mostly gets it, but sometimes suffers appalling headaches and then rages at everyone. They forgive him because of the hole in his head. What the females in the cast find less easy to tolerate is his habit of frequently popping into the ladies' dressing-room with a jolly shout of "It's only me, girls!" He makes his wife take a small part in every pantomime, though she can't act and can't remember either her lines or her moves.

"Come ON, Rose!" he bawls at her. "You know you move down *right* on that line. For heaven's sake *think*!" or "Speak up, Rose; I can't hear a word you say."

Aunt Gwen shakes her head sadly. "All that bawling only makes Rose more nervous and miserable," she says.

Aunt Gwen puts up with him partly out of sympathy and partly because, having been to dancing classes as a girl and been keen on ballet ever since, she enjoys training the chorus and anyway thinks it's all rather fun.

She meets the chorus between rehearsals, once a week in the village schoolroom, where the music teacher comes to play for them. By now they are supposed to know what to do, at least in the first scenes, so when they rehearse in the hall she stands in the wings "grinning like a Cheshire cat", she tells me, and calling out to make them smile, *smile*, SMILE!

Now she says "Come along. We'd better get back."

There is quite a crowd of people in the hall, talking away as if they were at a party. Megan sits alone, looking at her script.

"Come on, everybody. Prologue: the Christening. Let's get started," shouts Colonel Rivers.

An old man ("Mr Bates," Aunt Gwen tells me), who

has been reading his newspaper, taking no notice of anybody, gets up and goes to the piano. He runs his fingers up and down the keyboard and then strikes a few chords. (A bit out of tune and clanky, but he can't be blamed for the quality of his instrument). He fishes out a bundle of tattered music from his music-case, piles most of it on a chair beside him, sets Prologue and Act I music on the music-rest, lights his pipe and awaits orders.

Seven girls and women, of all shapes and sizes, aged from about sixteen to thirty, line up across the stage.

"Only seven of you! Who's missing?" asks Colonel Rivers.

"Cathy," answers one of the girls. "She can't come tonight. Her baby brother's poorly and her mum's gone to a whist drive, so she's had to stay and look after him."

I await an explosion of fury from the Colonel, but he only sighs and says "Well, you'll have to leave a gap where she's supposed to be."

Mr Bates strikes up the opening bars and the chorus break into a song of welcome and general jollity, with appropriate gestures, followed by a simple dance, vigorous if slightly untidy.

"SMILE!" yells Aunt Gwen from the wings. They obediently bare their teeth and then form a picturesque group upstage, on either side of the two chairs representing thrones.

They can be left alone for a while, so Aunt Gwen joins me in the hall in time for the entrance of the King ("the Vicar's son," she whispers) and Queen ("our grocer's daughter") who explain to each other about the imminent christening of their baby daughter, which seems to surprise them both.

Mr Bates then does his best to produce the semblance of a fanfare, to announce the entrance of the baby Princess, only it's not so much the baby who is announced as her nurse who is, of course, Colonel Rivers in plus-fours and tweed jacket, bearing a white bundle in his arms.

"Where's the cradle?" he demands and someone pushes on a cardboard box from the wings, downstage left, into which he carefully lays the royal infant.

"The cradle should be carried on by one of the chorus, just after their first song. Will you arrange that, Gwen?"

"Yes, all right, Douglas," Aunt Gwen calls back.

Now the Nurse – hands clasped over her stomach and head tilted to one side – gives us a soliloquy which I'm sure is screamingly funny to local people, for it's full of topical allusions, only I'm not local and can't understand the jokes, though I recognise the skill with which it's delivered. It's followed by a patter song, equally well put over, and then Enter Three Good Fairies, little girls from the local ballet class who know all about pointing their toes, rounding their arms and, of course, smiling. After dancing prettily for a bit (to one of those Palm Court tunes one knows so well but can never put a name to), they trip in turn to the cradle, to confer Beauty, Health and Happiness on the baby. At least, I think those are the gifts they confer though they are practically inaudible so I can't be sure. They start another dance but are interrupted by shuddering music followed by a crashing chord or two, and on leaps the Bad Fairy – Megan. Megan? This evil creature bears no resemblance to the cowed, gin-sodden girl we saw holding fast to the banisters as she crept down the dark staircase, or being scolded and pushed about by her elder sister. This is the Bad Fairy in person. She has even contrived to make herself ugly. She has discarded her coat and hat and has slung a black cloak over her shoulders which swirls about her as she glides and twists and leaps about the stage, uttering terrible imprecations. She is thin and lithe and gives authority even to the banal pantomime couplets she spits out with such venom. She bends over the cradle,

. . . the Nurse gives us a soliloquy

intones a final curse in a harsh, deep voice, and glides away.

I have just seen a true actress, a natural. Was it Aunt Gwen's black coffee or her own inventive, disciplined performance that brought about this transformation?

"Curtain!" shouts the Nurse. Some young man hauls at the tangle of old rope at the side of the stage but to no effect. The cast, frozen for a few seconds into attitudes of fear and consternation, relax into life as the Nurse and the King seize the edge of each curtain and tug with all their might. The curtains jerk, bit by bit, towards the centre, leaving a gap of a mere nine inches.

"I shall need two of you chaps to help me get that thing working properly," says Colonel Rivers. "We won't spend time on it now."

"It'll be All Right On The Night," says some wag and everyone laughs except the Colonel.

Then, "Well done, Megan," he calls out. "That was fine. The rest of you must be far more shocked and terrified, though."

I think they were probably as shocked and terrified as I was – too much so to adopt stereotyped gestures and expressions.

Colonel Rivers wants to repeat the opening chorus and dance, "to tidy it up a bit", but Aunt Gwen says she will do that next time she meets the girls, so he agrees to leave it to her and meanwhile to carry on with Act I. For this the spinning-wheel is required so, at a look from Aunt Gwen, I fetch it from the dressing-room cupboard and set it on stage near the Princess who has carried on a chair from which to operate it. The Princess is, of course, the Principal Girl and is now of marriageable age, given to singing popular songs and to spinning, for want of anything better to do. She is a pretty girl with quite a good stage presence and she now sings 'Over my shoulder goes one care' very charmingly. She then sits down to spin.

"How the dickens does this thing work?" she asks the Colonel.

"No idea," he replies. "Megan?"

Megan has no idea either, for she is never allowed to touch this valuable antique. At length it is made to work.

"But how does one prick one's finger on a spinning-wheel?" asks the Princess.

"I haven't the faintest idea," says the Colonel.

"I'll ask Bob," says Aunt Gwen. "He's sure to know. I should think it's something to do with the spike at the top of the distaff. Anyway, I know there ought to be wool on the distaff or what's the poor girl supposed to be spinning?"

Aunt Gwen believes Uncle Bob to know everything about everything, though I don't know how he can be expected to know about 'the distaff side'.

A slightly awkward King who hasn't learnt his lines and doesn't know what to do with his hands joins an exuberant and well-upholstered Queen in a popular though irrelevant song, supported by a chorus of courtiers and ladies-in-waiting. They are joined by the Nurse who, seizing a young courtier by the hand, pulls him downstage and they sing 'If you were the only girl in the world' together, with much ogling on the part of the Nurse, while the courtier does his best with a minimal tenor voice and languishing looks.

"It's done every year, a hardy perennial," murmurs Aunt Gwen. "The audience love it and it always gets an encore."

The Princess now gets back to her spinning and promptly pricks her finger, though no one knows what she pricks it on. "Ow!" she squeals and immediately expires. Everybody else falls dead too, though they are mostly standing up, like so many sleeping horses. On comes the Bad Fairy, laughing horribly as she views the corpses, and glides away, to be succeeded by the First Good Fairy who, though her powers are limited, succeeds in commuting the sentence of death to one of sleep. Nobody stirs but at least we know they are all alive.

The scene ends but this time nobody tries to operate the obstinate curtain. Instead, the Colonel makes one or two adjustments to the last grouping, but when he suggests repeating the whole thing, everyone droops at the very thought so he abandons the idea and gets Mr Bates to play a few tunes from *Top Hat,* one of which he chooses as the most suitable for his solo dance and tries out some fancy steps with surprising agility. Off-stage, the King lures the prettiest lady-in-waiting into a corner for an evidently private and urgent conversation. Aunt Gwen summons Megan and me to the picnic basket where the Bad Fairy tucks into the sandwiches as though she hasn't eaten for a week, while we confine ourselves to the remaining coffee and a few biscuits.

I compliment Megan on her performance and ask if she has done much acting.

"Not much," she says, "but I did play Viola at school and I've occasionally played with the Lee Dramatic Society when I can get there. It's difficult, though, because I don't drive and they rehearse about seven miles away."

"Can't one of your sisters take you?" I ask. "Or don't they drive either?"

"Oh, yes, they drive but they really haven't got time to bother and anyway Nesta doesn't like me to go out much."

(Good heavens! This isn't a child. She must be my age or a little older.)

Aunt Gwen says "You know, Megan, you have real talent. You shouldn't waste it. You should go to a drama school or join a repertory company or something."

94

"Nesta would never allow it. I'm surprised I've been allowed to take part in the pantomime even. We don't really mix with people."

Of course there's the gin-swigging, but I believe that if she were doing what she is obviously born to do Megan would drop drinking. She wouldn't need it any more. There must be other reasons we don't know about.

A row has broken out between Colonel Rivers and one Daphne Roberts, a buxom young woman who, I am told, is the Principal Boy.

"I've been hanging about doing nothing for hours," she says loudly. "You've rehearsed the Prologue and Act I several times already. If you didn't intend to do Act II you might have let me know. I have plenty to do at home."

"You know very well those early scenes needed rehearsing," replies Colonel Rivers, "and anyway who's producing this show? We can do a bit of Act II now, if you like."

"I don't like," says Daphne. "It's far too late and I'm tired. I'm going home."

She has been standing with legs apart, hands in her coat pockets, and I can quite picture her swaggering about the stage and slapping her thigh in the true Principal Boy manner. But now she turns about and strides out of the hall.

"Women!" mutters Colonel Rivers, and then loses his temper and shouts "Blasted women! She can go to blazes!"

An insignificant little woman I had hardly noticed comes up to him.

"Never mind, Douglas," she says, "I'm sure she'll be back."

"Oh, for God's sake shut up, Rose!" he snaps, and goes off into the wings. His wife starts to follow him, thinks better of it and, after the moment's silence that hangs heavily in the hall, smiles nervously at us all and whispers, "So sorry. He'll be better in a few minutes."

Dear, sensible Mr Bates plays a selection from *Bitter Sweet* quietly and soothingly and everybody starts talking together in an undertone.

"Daphne Roberts ought to have more sense," says Megan. "She knows how easily the Colonel gets upset. He can't help it, poor man."

One or two have a word with Mrs Rivers and then leave the hall. A few others just slip away. Most of us sit tight and wait.

Presently Colonel Rivers comes back onto the stage, calm but rather pale.

"Thank you, everybody," he says. "I think we'll call it a day. See you on Thursday. Thank you, Arthur," he calls to Mr Bates.

Mr Bates packs away his music, shuts the piano and, waving his pipe in a gesture of farewell towards everybody, goes off home. I daresay he is paid something for his time and his not inconsiderable ability, so I suppose he doesn't have to be talked to as well. Nobody takes much notice of the old boy.

We gather up the spinning-wheel and the picnic basket and go out to the car. There is a light drizzle falling.

"I expect there'll be some supper waiting for you when you get home, Megan?"

"Oh no," she says. "They'll have had supper. Your sandwiches were lovely, Mrs Richards. I shall just go to bed. Thank you for the lift."

We set her down by the great, dark house. She slips in and, like Nesta, shuts the front door before we drive away.

HOLIDAY TIME – 2

"I'VE asked my friend Alice Kelly to tea," Aunt Gwen tells me, "and her ten-year-old daughter, Faith. Alice is a bit cranky and peculiar – vegetarian and goes in for arty handicrafts and fancy religions – but I'm fond of her. I don't know the girl very well but she seems a bright little thing. They used to live in Sussex and then Edward, Alice's husband, died and they moved up here to be near a very unconventional school Alice seems to admire. It's called Meadowlands."

"Meadowlands? Isn't that where the children run wild and do no work?"

"That's what people say about it though I don't think it's altogether true. It's what they call 'progressive', I believe. They have about fifty boarders there and quite a lot of day-girls. Alice doesn't approve of sending children away to boarding school and anyway she couldn't afford one, so she's rented a little cottage about half a mile from Meadowlands, and Faith walks there and back every day. Whether she's actually learning anything I don't know. Perhaps we shall find out this afternoon. I told Alice I thought you'd be interested to hear about the place and I expect she'd be interested in your schools too." I doubt it.

Uncle Bob goes off to collect the guests who live some five miles away and haven't got a car. Young Faith will never know the fun of riding on the pillion of a bicycle. She and her mother will be driven sedately here in Uncle Bob's old Humber.

Aunt Gwen and I go out to welcome them. They are rather alike, with plain, friendly faces, though Mrs Kelly is tall and thin and looks as if life had given her a bit of a battering, while Faith is plumpish and cheerful.

When we are all in the drawing-room, we are told about Mrs Kelly's new friend, Diana Brandon, who lives at Meadowlands and teaches art there.

" 'Brandysnap'," Faith interposes with a grin.

"That's a bit of cheek," says Uncle Bob, "I bet you don't call her that to her face."

"Oh, yes," says Faith, "all the mistresses are called by their nicknames, except Mrs Christopher, the Headmistress. Only the Seniors are allowed to call her Chrissy. Go on Mother, tell them what you do with Brandysnap."

"Well, she's a talented young woman and she lets me go along to the Art Barn and learn about modelling and barbola work and watercolours. It's the greatest fun. Of course I asked Mrs Christopher about it and she doesn't seem to mind."

I ask about the school.

"It's mostly all right," says Faith decisively. "It's much better than my last school. That was all stupid rules and punishments and hardly ever being allowed to talk or ask questions."

"What do you like doing best?" asks Uncle Bob.

"I like most things, really, except boring old history. And French. I like doing experiments in the lab with Mrs Critchley. She teaches science and botany and sometimes she takes us out for walks and that's simply marvellous because she's awfully nice – really *decent* – and she really makes you notice what's going on everywhere. She tells us about trees and plants and animals and things.''

"What about arithmetic?'' asks Aunt Gwen, with that teasing smile people put on because they generally assume all children hate the subject.

"Oh, I quite like that. Polly teaches us (that's Mr Parrott) and he teaches us carpentry too. He's better at it than Brandysnap, but they're both all right. They sort of take it in turns.''

"If you like carpentry, perhaps you'd like to see my workshop?'' Undle Bob suggests.

"Oh, yes I would,'' says Faith and stands up. They go off together.

Mrs Kelly asks me about my schools, though I can tell she isn't really interested and anyway, though I've left Fettington Court and don't mind talking about it (especially as I despise the place), I have a rather priggish reluctance to prattle about the schools at which I still work. Mrs Kelly is only too pleased to go on telling us about Meadowlands which has become her main interest.

We learn that, while Mrs Christopher is the inspiration behind it all, neither she nor her staff exert much authority. The school is mainly run by a Committee of five senior girls, democratically elected by all the children and led by a Chairman. On the morning of her election each girl has to stand up before the whole school and make a solemn promise to serve faithfully and conscientiously. She then has a brown leather badge pinned on her by Mrs Christopher. Her term of office lasts a year, though she can be re-elected for a further year. She is supposed to be guide, philosopher and friend to everybody, even the youngest, and no bossier than absolutely necessary.

There are no rules at Meadowlands, only Traditions, though I don't quite know what these are. Anyone who departs from a 'tradition' (i.e. anyone who has been naughty), is spoken to with sweet reasonableness by one of the Committee and, apparently, is nearly always brought to see the error of her ways. A persistently tiresome child is sometimes required by one of the Committee to take the school goat for a walk. She drags it (or is dragged by it) at the end of a rope and, since it is an obstinate and rather vicious creature, she generally persuades one or two of her friends to help.

"But, apart from skipping a lesson or two, the children seem to behave themselves," Mrs Kelly says.

It's Chrissy's devotion to Fresh Air that both children and staff find hard to bear. Unless it's raining or snowing or blowing a gale, all lessons are held in the garden, however cold the weather. The girls have to carry their desks outside and then, if it rains, lug them in again. Once indoors, they sit with the windows wide open and aren't allowed near the only fire. The young Matron (unqualified but kindly) is constantly treating colds and chilblains. What's even worse, it seems, (according to Faith and her mother's friend, Brandysnap), is the morning ritual. When everyone has assembled for Prayers in the morning (staff on chairs at the back, girls sitting on the floor), Chrissy makes her entrance and all stand. The windows, of course, are wide open. With hands clasped round ribs, everyone does breathing exercises, including Chrissy who seems to withstand the cold that makes everyone else's eyes water and their noses sting.

Then, when all are sitting down again, Chrissy reads a passage from Tagore, St Paul, Kahlil Gibran, Traherne, Annie Besant, Proverbs or anything with a bit of moral uplift that Chrissy happens to fancy that day. The reading is followed by a hymn and then one of the staff gives a short talk. All the mistresses have to do this and, while some quite enjoy it, others are miserably nervous. Faith has told her mother of poor 'Riddles' (Miss Ridler) who managed to get through a story about a shipwreck, in the course of which a cowardly and irresponsible seaman

100

was drowned. It ended with the moving lines, 'And bubbles rose . . . and he was no more!' uttered in a thin little voice but with great dramatic feeling which, says her mother, Faith and her friends faithfully and cruelly repeated all over the school for weeks afterwards.

I can't remember whether it's at the first or the last Prayers of the year that Chrissy always delivers her most important Talk, though I'm sure Mrs Kelly told us. It is then that the girls are told of the importance of Ideas and how they should lead to the driving force of Ideals. "You *must* Dream," she insists. I daresay many of them do, though possibly not in the constructive way she intends.

"She's a remarkable woman," says Mrs Kelly, "and people respect her even though they also laugh at her. I'm pleased to say she's a vegetarian, like me, and so are most of the children and a few of the staff. Faith is vegetarian when she's at home but I'm afraid she does eat meat at school, mainly because her beloved Mrs Critchley is a meat-eater and, in Faith's eyes, she can do no wrong. I think Chrissy would like the whole school to be vegetarian but I suppose she's afraid of losing pupils if it was, and probably some of the staff as well."

We ask if there's a Mr Christopher anywhere about and are told he's an amiable old man, known to everyone as 'Pop', and he and his wife have their own private rooms in the school, though he is seldom seen indoors. He is groundsman, gardener and handyman, bumbles about the place on his own and talks to anyone who bothers to talk to him. Not many people do. He seems to be simply a piece of garden furniture.

It occurs to me that, if Pop is a groundsman, he must have grounds to care for and indeed the girls do play hockey and tennis if they feel so inclined. They don't seem to play matches but perhaps there are no other schools for them to meet. Those who don't like games go for walks instead. Faith is one of them.

Uncle Bob and Faith come in for tea. He is making a picture frame for a local artist friend and has been introducing Faith to the art of mitring. She is full of excitement and admiration.

". . . and it's all so *tidy*," she tells her mother. "All those lovely clean tools hung up in rows. And the things Bob has made! Boats and book-ends and even a gramophone he made years ago and which still works."

"Mr Richards to you, Faith," her mother reproves her.

"Or perhaps 'Uncle' Bob," suggests Aunt Gwen.

"But he's not my uncle," Faith points out, very reasonably.

"Oh, never mind," says Uncle Bob. "I answer to Hi or to any loud cry." The subject of courteous address is allowed to drop and Faith tells us about the school workshop which is always in an awful muddle so that no one can find anything, least of all Polly.

"In that case you'd better tidy it up, see that the tools are cleaned and put in order, and put up a notice threatening anyone found leaving them about or not cleaning them after use with some dire punishment."

"I might try," says Faith, "but I don't know that Polly and the others would let me interfere in there."

Aunt Gwen and I talk about the pantomime and give impressions of some of the performers. She is particularly good as the Nurse and I have a try at the King. Faith laughs, but her mother only manages a pained smile.

"Such a travesty of those lovely old stories, I always think," she says, "and such terrible drivel. Still, I suppose you enjoy it, Gwen, or you wouldn't bother."

She sips her pale, milkless China tea and toys with a little brown bread and butter. I'm glad she doesn't discourage her daughter from tucking in to everything that's going. Aunt Gwen, as I well remember, knows all about schoolgirls' appetites and she and Lily have laid on a really good spread.

102

We are told about a play produced by the Seniors last term, written by one of the girls and based on an Indian legend.

"Did you enjoy it, Faith?" I ask.

"Oh, yes. It was simply marvellous. Lovely dresses and scenery and golden lights and they all spoke in loud, actory sort of voices. The only thing was, I didn't really know what it was about, so I felt a bit disappointed at the end."

"I've been to plays like that too," I assure her.

Uncle Bob goes back to his frame-making, the other two settle down for some cosy reminiscences and Faith and I go for a walk. She notices and names every bird we see, and many of the trees and plants too, but not in a showing-off way. She is simply interested in everything and I feel ashamed of my own ignorance.

"How do you know so much about nature?" I ask.

"It's Nokomis – that's Mrs Critchley. She makes everything so interesting, so *important*. She says most people go about with their eyes and ears and noses tight shut. She's quite right. I did too until she taught me how to notice things. She really is simply marvellous."

"Why did you call her Nokomis?"

"Well, we've got this group called 'The Morning Stars', which is sort of to do with Red Indians and Hiawatha. We wear brown tunics and sew coloured beads on them in patterns, and we have bands round our heads with feathers stuck into them, and we have tracking and camp fires and cooking and we learn how to recognise things. And we each have a Red Indiany sort of name. Mrs Critchley is Nokomis and she's the Chief. I'm Silver Birch."

We walk on in silence for a while. Then I ask her why she hates history and French.

"Old Ringworm (that's Miss Wrington) is so *boring*," she says. "On and on about dull old kings and wars that

103

happened ages and ages ago. I don't care what happened in those days.''

"Well, what's wrong with learning French?" I ask. "That's not ages ago. People talk it today."

"Oh, we aren't taught how to *talk* it. We just do verbs and short sentences about something we don't want to say. Anyway, I don't want to go to France. I skip French whenever I can."

"Don't you get into trouble?"

"I've had a pi-jaw from one of the Committee about missing History, and Nosey-Hairpins sometimes chases after me and screams and yells. I don't care."

"Nosey-Hairpins?" I enquire.

"That's Mamzelle. She's French, with a red, pointed nose and her hairpins keep falling out of the buns she wears over her ears. That's why we call her Nosey-Hairpins, but only behind her back of course. She's not a bad old thing, but who wants to talk French, for goodness' sake?"

Without much hope, and trying not to sound too school-marmy, I ask about other subjects. Chrissy teaches English and that, it seems is "not too bad". An Italian lady with a wobbly voice takes them for choral singing, which Faith enjoys, and a young Miss Simpkins teaches Margaret Morris dancing which, I'm told, is based on attitudes copied from ancient Egyptian tombs and vases.

"It's a bit silly," says Faith, "but quite fun. Miss Simpkins is fairly decent and awfully *supple*. Between classes she tries out positions in front of the hall mirror and admires herself no end."

Then there's a Mrs Barrington who teaches Elocution, always wears a hat and lots of beads and "booms away like anything", but she doesn't teach Faith. No doubt she accounts for the actory voices in the school play.

For the rest of our walk we don't talk much. Faith kicks leaves about, peers at a sinister-looking fungus under a tree, examines a badger's sett and watches two rabbits scamper away. I brood on schools, teachers and children, having long ago come to the conclusion that children who don't want to learn won't, whether they play truant or gaze out of the classroom window during lessons, and even those who are charmed or coerced into working at school soon forget what they have learned. Never mind; something remains – an influence, an attitude, perhaps some curiosity. Faith is only ten but it seems likely that her main interests will last all her life, thanks mainly to Mrs Critchley. It's even possible that, when she is older, those interests may be extended to include entirely different matters.

When Faith and I get back, Mrs Kelly says it's time they went home. Aunt Gwen says, "Do forgive me, Alice, if I don't come too. Bob will take you. I've so many little jobs to do here." They press their cheeks together and Faith suffers a peck on hers and manages an awkward "Thank you for having me".

As Uncle Bob and his passengers disappear down the drive, Aunt Gwen collapses onto the sofa.

"Dear Alice," she says; "she's a splendid woman and she's had quite a hard life. She was always a serious girl and now she's become so terribly earnest it's really rather exhausting. She wants me to join something called 'The Circle of Enlightenment'. I'm afraid she thinks me terribly shallow and frivolous. Well, I expect I am. I don't particularly want to be enlightened. I just want to live here with Bob, potter about the garden, read a few books, see one or two friends, deal with Douglas Rivers and that 'low' pantomime once a year and – well, that's about all really."

"I'm so glad," I tell her. "I couldn't bear it if you took to Enlightenment and barbola."

When he comes back Uncle Bob says, "I don't know how you tolerate that woman, Gwen. She's not normal.

Just because I enjoy making things, I've been given a patronising lecture about 'the dignity of work'.''

"Did Faith have anything to say?" I ask.

"No. She has more sense. She's a cheeky little thing, but she has her head screwed on. And she's good with her hands. I gave her one or two jobs to do in the workshop and she got the hang of them at once."

"Don't you think, Bob," says Aunt Gwen in a weary voice, "that we could all have a drink for once?"

"Excellent notion," says Uncle Bob, and presently the two of them have a whisky apiece and I have a glass of sherry.

NOW I'm back in London. I had two more days of blissful laziness during which nobody mentioned pantomimes, children or Higher Thought. Aunt Gwen and I just sat by the fire, reading and occasionally talking, while dear Uncle Bob inspected my car: checked the plugs, the tyres, the oil and petrol and advised me to stop in the village for a couple of gallons, on my way home. Then he and Aunt Gwen waved me away.

My flat feels cold and desolate and the larder is practically bare. I should have stocked up in the village. I light the gas fire, find one curly rasher of bacon, two eggs and a packet of biscuits, make coffee (thank goodness the milkman has left me a pint) and settle down to eat and make a shopping list. O Lily, where art thou?

PART II

Spring, 1939

CRANSTEAD SCHOOL – 2

WE are well into the Spring Term, though spring is undoubtedly 'far behind'. The windows rattle as rain lashes the panes in fierce gusts. Every now and then a wisp of smoke is puffed into the classroom from the little cairn of coal in the grate, and wind whistles dismally round the ill-fitting door.

The children of Form III sneeze, sniff, cough, but do not complain. Winter is always cold and, at Cranstead School, colder than anywhere else. That's life and they have learnt to accept it. Not for them the luxury of central heating or cheerful gas fires.

Cranstead is a battle-field. I am flung into a weekly skirmish which never has time to develop into war, much less to reach conclusive victory or defeat. One of my foes is Miss Rook. She fights me with an innate distrust of the arts (Miss Emily's piano and class-singing lessons are considered relatively harmless), with snobbery and her Repetition classes. The other foes are parents, particularly Mothers, whose influence is obviously more potent in a day-school than when, as boarders – and there are only about half a dozen of these – they are out of parental reach during termtime. There are doting mums, indifferent mums, unkind mums, ambitious mums, society mums. I have met none of them but I know them well through their children. I can only fight back with tact, belief in my job, tact, patience and tact.

Jane is, as it were, the spearhead of Form III Repetition. She has a memory like a sponge and it is not difficult for her to mug up as much of the Bible and of speeches from Shakespeare as even Miss Rook could wish. If I ask for anything else to be memorised, she is always the girl who is word perfect and proud of it. She can let out a stream of words at high speed and with deadly accuracy. She gives no thought to their meaning and they signify nothing to her or to anyone else, but in Repetition that doesn't matter and it therefore seems unreasonable of me to expect her to understand – let alone enjoy – anything she belts out. Repetition is a daily lesson. What hope have I with my weekly twenty minutes?

Helen's mummy, so her daughter once told me, won local fame in her youth with her monologues and is evidently determined that Helen shall follow in her melodramatic footsteps. She coaches her at home, with the result that my labours are in vain. It is people like Helen and her mother who have brought the word 'elocution' into disrepute. Here are the soulful incantation, the mouthings, the 'golden voice', the attitude of ecstasy so beloved of an earlier generation.

Annabel and Peggy, on the other hand, have the gift of self-effacement. They sit at the back of the class, quietly scribbling all over their blotting-paper. It is difficult to remember they are there. They seldom do any work but we once put on a play in which they actually took part, enjoyed it and were justifiably proud of their achievement. Their parents didn't bother to come and see them in it.

Then there is Fenella who, being the daughter of an Earl, is Miss Rook's treasure. She is a clever, sophisticated little piece and seems to attend countless gymkhanas and parties. Her main interests lie in horses, clothes and film stars, and

. . . the soulful incantation

she has considerable charm of manner. She once told me that her mother has a horror of gauche, giggly schoolgirls and of intellectual women. Consequently, Fenella uses her brain as sparingly as possible and her precocious poise conceals a void of ignorance and immaturity. She is like a cake baked in too hot an oven, of which the outside is nicely browned and the centre, an uncooked, soggy mass. Fenella, in fact, provides one of the arguments in favour of boarding-schools (though I don't believe these to be best for every type of child) in which the baking is often slower and more thorough.

Sarah too, I believe, would do better away from home. She blushes easily, has a nervous twitch and is a kind, sensible, slow, unclever girl whose mother, a Ph.D., is determined her daughter shall have a distinguished academic career, for which she has neither inclination nor ability. What is constantly and affectionately said of her, and I believe always will be, is 'Poor old Sarah!'

Most of the children, I admit, are not so parent-ridden and are able to develop naturally and individually, at least as far as is possible within the narrow confines of Cranstead. I try to mitigate the effects of the dreaded Repetition in the limited time allowed me. At least they seem to enjoy my efforts.

After Form III I go down to the school hall, where twenty small boys (pre-prep-school) and girls are waiting for me, sitting in a semi-circle on the floor, under the motherly eye of Mrs Young. She is a pleasant, rather shy girl, young in years as well as in name (about my age in fact) but 'motherly' is the word for her. The children behave like little angels so long as she is in the room but, as soon as she leaves and I am in charge, trouble starts as it always does. I am unable to cope with five-year-olds except singly. *En masse* I find them unnerving and exasperating.

This morning they are worse than usual and so am

I. Nicholas, who has large brown eyes and a charming smile, creeps up and unzips my dress from neck to hem, revealing my less-than-elegant underwear. As I struggle to do it up again, the children jump about in an ecstasy of glee. Peter pinches Miranda and makes her howl, Robert and Rosemary perform like Dervishes and the two Michaels become a very noisy express train. Eventually order is restored, after which I hear myself sounding more and more revoltingly winsome every minute.

We start away, however, and I am beginning to feel quite pleased with the fun we are all having when Catherine suddenly announces ''I had a puppy for my birfday. He's called Patchy.''

''Our dog's called Wrinkles,'' says John.

''What a silly name!'' says Rosemary.

'''Tisn't silly.''

'''Tis.''

'''Tisn't.''

''Please may I be excused?'' asks Timothy.

''Ow! John kicked me,'' whines Rosemary.

''Tell-tale-tit,'' chants Catherine.

''May I be excused?'' asks Robert.

''No, you mayn't. I asked first and I want to go,'' says Timothy. ''Badly,'' he adds, plaiting his legs to prove it.

Between and after these interruptions, we are able to enjoy a few rhymes and a story.

When Mrs Young returns, gentle and smiling, the prattle stops at once. The children line up quietly, smile at me politely and leave the room in good order. I wish I knew how she does it.

When I think of the thousands of women who teach twice that number of infants all day every day, for years, I am filled with shame and admiration. Twenty minutes of that little lot and I'm exhausted.

STANDISH LODGE - 2

PROVIDENTIALLY, Miss James wrote to me just after Christmas, to ask if I could spend another half day at Standish Lodge, as two more children had asked for private lessons and she also wanted me to take a play-reading class with the Sixth Form. She could, of course, pay me *pro rata* for this extra time. I should have to spend one night a week at the school so as to start the lessons first thing in the morning.

I was pleased. I didn't like the idea of sleeping away from home but the extra money would fill part of the Fettington void and, besides, I enjoyed teaching at Standish.

IT is not until after tea that I am able to find out where I am to sleep tonight. Eggy takes me up to the sick wing and shows me into a smallish room opening off the main dormitory. Happily, both rooms are free of patients but, this being the spring term, there will almost certainly be a 'flu epidemic and probably various other infectious diseases to fill all the beds, so where shall I go then? Sufficient unto the day . . . Eggy leaves me to unpack and get settled.

At Standish Lodge there is central heating on the ground floor but none upstairs. The room is icy and everything in it is white, which makes it seem even colder. I turn back the bedspread and find two thin, white blankets beneath. I sit on the bed and its springs sound like the opening of a dungeon door in a Victorian thriller. Altogether, this is not the kind of room to make a sick child feel happy and comfortable.

I remember hearing that the staff always change for supper, so I have pushed a Little Dress into my suitcase. Now I take it out and it looks as if it had been slept in for a week. I hang it from a hook on the door, though I fear the creases will probably freeze in rather than hang out, and go thankfully down to the Fifth Form and warmth.

When lessons are over it is time to return to my refrigerator, to change. To tear off my twin-set and skirt and plunge into a frock calls for resolution and courage. When I go to the bathroom, to wash, the hot tap makes gurgling noises and exudes a little tepid, brownish liquid which I rub onto my face and hands and transfer to a fragment of towel. Back in the bedroom, with the lofty, white-shaded light behind me, the mirror reveals a dark blob where my face should be, so I squint into my handbag mirror, do what I can with comb and make-up, and shiver my way down to supper.

The huge dining-room is dim and empty except where, in one corner, a patch of light falls on a table laid for the staff. (The girls have already had their last meal of the day). It is probably warm in here, but by now I am so cold that only an oven could have any effect on me. Eggy, Rachel Strong and Margaret Anderton are already standing by their chairs.

"Welcome, little stranger," says Rachel, looking willowy and elegant in hyacinth blue. "Come and sit beside me so I can see you 'be'ave proper'."

Eggy and Margaret flash their glasses at me in a friendly manner. Eggy is in purple, with layers of frills augmenting the curve of her bosom and dangling from her wrists, and

. . . a dark blob where my face should be

Margaret's dress is a shade of pale green that does nothing for her greenish complexion. We are presently joined by Rosemary Gedge, trim and unobtrusive in beige, and by Fraulein Hartmann whose clinging mauve garment is strained over the bulges of her person and the ridges of her winter underwear. She is closely followed by Miss James and Miss Browne, the one in brown velvet instead of the usual brown wool; the other in deep crimson upon which life-sized sunflowers have erupted in startling profusion. I myself am in a rust-coloured dress which has seen better days. I decide that we all look much better in our ordinary old jerseys and skirts.

We have just sat down when Zelly bursts upon us, breathless with haste and apologies, scintillating with marquesite, her grey hair swept up into a frenzy of combs and undulations, the air about her vibrant with scent and her neat plumpness encased in a little black number of impeccable simplicity. Miss James smiles her acceptance of the apologies, Miss Browne looks at Zelly with the expression of one who finds the milk has turned, and Rachel grows pink with suppressed giggles. Margaret coughs a little as the scent catches her throat.

One cannot say that staff supper is exactly formal, but it is certainly something of a strain. Miss James says little and eats less. I rather think she is shy of anyone over the age of eighteen. She answers quite pleasantly any remarks addressed to her and then falls back into silence, without trying to develop a conversation, smiling amiably round the table in a deceptively absent-minded way. Her presence, together with Miss Browne's habit of putting the worst possible construction on everything that is said, makes everyone self-conscious. We all take such pains to appear natural that we talk and laugh to excess and try to put ourselves over to Miss James and Miss Browne as the people we hope they think us. This is not deception so much as self-defence.

When the meal is over, Miss Browne sits sucking her teeth and Fraulein heaves intermittently with indigestion. Following Miss James' lead, we all leave the table and, when she and Miss Browne have bidden us goodnight and withdrawn to their own suite (known to the rest of us as 'the Holies'), we amble along to the staff-room. I crouch by the fire.

"You needn't think you're going to stay there," says Rachel. "You're coming out with Zelly and me."

I tell her firmly that nothing and nobody will move me from the fire.

"You are coming with us to call on Fanné," says Zelly, as though I had not spoken. "She always has a beeg fire and deleecious coffee and I am taking a bottle of wine."

"Who's Fanny?" I ask, my resolution starting to waver.

"Good grrracious! She asks who is Fanné!" exclaims Zelly.

"I thought even you would know about Fanny," says Rachel, "but of course you and she are never here on the same days. She's been teaching here since about 1066 – biology, botany, general science. Her name's Mrs Fanshawe and she's a poppet. Come on, I promise you'll enjoy yourself."

I protest that I want to stay by the fire, that I have work to do, that Mrs Fanshawe won't want to be landed with a complete stranger. Rachel and Zelly wait.

I go to fetch my coat.

It is a bitterly cold evening. We bury our chins in our coat collars and Rachel and I start briskly down the road till Zelly's plaintive wails force us to slow down. She is teetering along on her high heels, clutching the bottle of wine to her bosom and gasping for breath. Her finery is hidden under a baggy old tweed coat but this does nothing to quench the scent which hangs about her even more powerfully than before in the cold, windless air.

Mrs Fanshawe lives in a small terrace house. She is a

skinny, round-shouldered little person with white hair and startlingly blue eyes. She seems unsurprised and pleased to see us, even though she already has another guest, a dark, brooding woman with a dark, brooding voice, called Mrs Nelson, the mother of Jean, one of the day-girls at the school.

As Zelly promised, there is 'a beeg fire and deleecious coffee'. Mrs Fanshawe sets the bottle of wine by the hearth, to recover from its journey.

Mrs Nelson gazes at me deeply.

"Of course my Jean simply *adores* your lessons," she says. "She's such a sensitive, highly-strung child and your work gives her a kind of *release*. D'you know what I mean?"

"Yes," I say, feeling uncomfortable and trying to give the single word a wealth of meaning. I dare not glance at Rachel or Zelly for it is a longstanding staff-room joke that the mother hardly exists who doesn't think her child more sensitive and highly strung than anyone else's.

"Jean is a nice, normal child," says Fanny briskly but not unkindly. "Don't fantasticate so, Leah."

Mrs Nelson laughs indulgently and gives me a conspiratorial look. I smile understandingly back.

Fanny steers the conversation towards the others and while they talk I have time to look about. We are in a small, colourless, untidy room with an ugly fireplace. There is not much space for the five of us for, on one side of the bay window stands an upright piano piled with music, on the other side is a gramophone and a rack full of records, and there are built-in bookshelves on either side of the fireplace. On the mantelpiece a tarnished silver clock ticks companionably between two curly picture-postcards and a brown jug with a bundle of letters pushed behind it. On one wall hangs a picture of Brahms playing the piano and, on another, an old flower print.

The talk flows as easily as a shallow stream. In spite of Mrs Nelson, it has no sombre depths, nor does it sparkle with wit or tinkle with polite inanities. Fanny has the gift of making her guests feel both relaxed and alert so that we seem to ourselves and each other to be a little wiser than usual.

While we drink the wine, she plays to us – Bach and Poulenc. She sits quite still, crouched over the keyboard like a small, attentive monkey, and though her hands move, she plays with such ease that they seem to have nothing to do with the intricate, flawless music. Mrs Nelson lies back and listens with her eyes closed. Rachel blinks at the fire. She is such a pleasure to look at that I have to keep glancing at her: her smooth, young face with the neat nose and kind mouth, her fair hair and incongruously large and capable hands. Zelly has kicked off her shoes and sits with ankles crossed, staring at her toes.

When Fanny leaves the piano, the talk turns to teaching. Mrs Nelson wants to know why each of us became a teacher. Our answers must disappoint her for none of us is able to declare that she had had 'a call', that teaching is her vocation. Zelly started, partly because she wanted to come to England, being a devoted Anglophile, and partly to escape the clutches of a tyrannical mother. Rachel trained at Bedford College because it seemed that teaching was the only way she could go on playing games and doing gym after she left school. I had drifted into teaching because I needed financial independence and lacked the nerve to risk poverty in the Theatre – sweeping the stage and painting scenery (I never wanted to be a professional actress) – in the hope of becoming, eventually, a producer of extraordinarily original and exciting plays. Fanny, I notice, takes no part in these confessions and I should have liked to learn something of her history.

Mrs Nelson looks depressed. "Cheer up, Leah," says

Fanny. "It's just possible we may not be as bad at our job as you fear. On the other hand, we may be even worse."

"There's always Margaret Anderton," says Rachel. "I bet she started teaching her dolls when she was about three and she'll go on teaching till she's ninety. She's absolutely dedicated."

"Eggy also," says Zelly, "and the children love her."

Soon after this we take our leave.

"Come round any time you feel like it," Fanny says to me as she sees us out. "Don't wait to be asked or brought by the others."

I thank her and, glowing with warmth, wine and sociability, follow Rachel and Zelly out into the bitter night.

When we get back to school, we find we have been locked out and nobody has remembered to bring a key. We try all the doors and several windows. Rachel and I start laughing. Zelly gets crosser and crosser. At last Rachel manages to open a cloakroom window, hoists herself onto the window-sill and drops onto the lockers inside.

Zelly teeters about under the window like a demented hen. She scrabbles ineffectually at the wall and the sill.

"But I *can't*, I *can't*, voyons!" she keeps repeating. "I am not a monké." At last she manages to heave herself up towards the window, and promptly slithers down again, scraping the toes of her shoes.

"Merde!" says Zelly.

"Rachel!" I call, as loud as I dare, "Rachel, why not go and open the door?"

There is a suppressed gurgle of laughter from the cloakroom, followed by a stage whisper.

"Good Lord!" says Rachel. "I never thought of that!"

I escort the furious Zelly to the side door and Rachel lets us into the dark and silent house. Zelly, muttering oaths, tiptoes upstairs. Rachel and I creep along to the staff-room to warm up again, but only a few faintly glowing embers remain in the grate and the scuttle is empty.

"Come up to my room," says Rachel. We go quietly upstairs and, not daring to switch on any lights, grope our way along corridors, past silent dormitories. Her study-bedroom is no warmer than the staff-room, but it has an electric fire and we kneel on the rug in front of it.

"Thank you for taking me to Fanny's," I say. "I enjoyed myself. She's a dear."

"Going over to Fanny's is one of the few things that keep me sane in this place."

"Really? I thought you liked it here."

"Oh, I do, I do, but there's something about that staff-room, night after night, that jangles the nerves, and we are rather discouraged from keeping to our own rooms and burning fires for too long."

"What about the others? Do they have their nerves jangled too?"

Rachel thought for a moment. "Eggy likes the matiness of the staff-room. Margaret is so busy preparing lessons and correcting books that she doesn't notice what goes on there. Frauly hates it, but then the poor old thing is so homesick she couldn't be happy anywhere away from Frankfurt. Zelly prattles away to anyone likely or unlikely to listen, and Rosemary keeps smiling and making polite conversation, but, I'm sure, mostly lives in her own private world."

It's past midnight. I drag myself away from the warmth, slip out of the room and make my way to the sick-wing.

The cold of my white room presses solidly against me. I fill my hot-water bottle from the tepid tap, spread my coat over the bed, rush into my pyjamas, put on a cardigan over them, clean my chattering teeth and then slide between the icy sheets, shivering violently. Oh, blast! I haven't put the light out. I get up and run to the switch by the door. Back in bed, I lie curled up like a wood-louse, trying to pluck up courage to push my feet down to even colder depths and trying to find a hollow between the lumps in the mattress in which to settle my hip. What bliss it will be to lie in my own snug bed tomorrow night!

I must have fallen asleep for suddenly I'm startled by the screaming of an electric bell on the landing. Fire? No; getting up time I suppose. The bed now seems voluptuously warm and comfortable. It takes me longer to make up my mind to get up than to get dressed. I wash briefly and superficially, glad for hygienic as well as for all the other reasons, that I am to spend only one night a week here. The gong booms. I slap on powder and lipstick and hurry down to the dining-room.

Miss James and Miss Browne do not appear at breakfast. Eggy presides and the rest of us sit at the ends of the other tables. The children chatter merrily as they tuck into bacon and fried bread, followed by innumerable doorsteps of bread and jam.

"I say, Miss Garth, are you always going to stay now?"

"Miss Garth, d'you know what Betty said yesterday? She said – um . . ."

"It's Mummy's birthday on Tuesday, Miss Garth, and . . ."

"My mummy's birthday's in June – no, July – no, June . June the 12th."

"Gosh, Trix, so's my mummy's. Shake." They solemnly shake hands.

"I say, Miss Garth, Betty said . . ."

I pin a smile on, sip my tea, raise my eyebrows, shake my head, nod and from time to time say "Good gracious!" or "Really?" or "How lovely!" though I am still barely awake. A glance across at Zelly and Rachel shows me that they are in much the same state. They smile and sip, their eyes glassy. Only Eggy talks happily with her

123

neighbours but then, they are Seniors and anyway she was probably not up till after midnight.

Afterwards, when we have made our beds, we assemble for prayers. The staff stand in a row at the side of the hall and stare at the ranks of girls who gaze into space, cough, fidget or dream. Rosemary sits at the piano and we wait in comparative silence for the arrival of Miss James and Miss Browne. Nina drops her hymnbook, blushes furiously as she bends to pick it up and then starts to giggle. This sets her neighbours off into paroxysms of suppressed mirth. Bunty has lost a hair-ribbon and stands, defiantly self-conscious, with a lock falling over her face. After prayers, she will no doubt be 'spoken to' by one of the prefects. These stand, trim and serious, apparently gazing straight ahead but no doubt noticing the slightest misdemeanour.

Miss Browne surges in and I nearly give her the applause accorded to the leader of an orchestra. A few seconds later, the conductor, Miss James, appears, slightly inclines her head and says "Good morning, everybody." Staff and girls reply in chorus.

Rosemary plays the opening bars of 'New every morning is the love' and we all burst into song. Frauly, standing beside me, improvises an alto part which only occasionally blends harmonically with the melody, or so it seems to me, though I can't be sure for her voice has such a pronounced wobble that it is difficult to decide which of two or three notes she is supposed to be singing at any one time.

Margaret Savage, Form IV, reads the lesson not too badly but not quite well enough. I resolve to devote more time to Bible reading. While Miss James reads some prayers, I start thinking of the few people I know who read the Bible well and the many who read it badly. Then the Lord's Prayer breaks out around me and I join in, wondering what everybody is thinking as we rattle off those familiar words, which leads me to wonder why I am wondering instead of thinking about the prayer. When we have said "Fo rever an dever amen" and Miss James has blessed us, she exhorts the girls to go up and down stairs *quietly* and to SHUT LAVATORY DOORS. (This particular plea is made constantly and ineffectually at every school I go to). Then she sails out of the room and the girls file out after her, watched by the Head Girl who barks out the name of anyone who speaks or giggles or pulls someone's plait. I slip round Frauly and come alongside Eggy.

"Eggy *dear*," I whisper. "Next week can I sleep anywhere but in the refrigerator I was in last night? *Please*."

"Were you cold?" she asks in surprise.

"Cold? I was frozen to the sheets. They had to hack me out with an ice-pick this morning."

"Oh, dear," says Eggy. "there's nowhere else I'm afraid."

"What about an electric fire?"

"There's no point for it. Of course," she says doubtfully, "there's the guest room."

"Well?"

"Well, it's in the Holies. I don't think . . ."

"Oh, all right," I say. "Forget it. I'll manage."

No member of the staff or school ever penetrates to the Holies unless summoned for a ticking-off, except on Parents' Days and other social occasions. No doubt the guest room is luxurious, always supposing I was allowed to use it, but I should feel out of place there and there would certainly be no more slipping in at midnight.

Eggy looks distressed and I'm sorry I complained.

By now the girls are gone. We follow them out and go to our respective classrooms to start the day's work.

RINGER'S END – 2

THE house smells of damp spaniel. Caesar is stretched beside the Courtier stove in the hall, after a constitutional waddle through wet grass. Mrs Minton has a cold and looks all of her age, in spite of the trim blue skirt and dusty-pink jumper and pearls. Her hair is flat and dull and there are dark roots among the weary gold. Miss Tarrant appears tired and worried and Dorothy Andrews tells me (when an opportunity occurs to deliver the Stop Press News) that it is because Robby is retreating further and further into her private world of remembered African horrors and because a gossipy parent has reported that Simmy entertained an Indian gentleman at her cottage for a week during the holidays. Dorothy herself is suffering the pangs of unrequited love. Ruth alone remains brisk and cheerfully scornful of the troubles around her and of the establishment as a whole.

Most of the children are restless and listless and several are in bed with 'flu. I tell myself that this is where a visiting teacher should sweep through the school like a summer breeze – cheering, calming, enlivening and refreshing. I do my best, but the reaction of my colleagues and pupils is not encouraging. This does not surprise me, for the more I am infected by their depression, the more obviously artificial grow my efforts. IIB, however, are as irrepressible as ever.

"I say, Miss Garth," says Penelope Studely, pop-eyed and agog, "Miss Robinson's gone potty."

The rest of IIB tell her to shut up, as I do, though in more seemly language.

"D'you know, Miss Garth," says Victoria – partly to create a diversion because she is fond of Robbie and partly because she wants me to take notice of her – "D'you know, when I was in France last hols I had wine every day for lunch because nobody drinks water there because it's poison."

"Oh, stale *buns*," says Susan, "everybody knows that. Anyway, I had beer when I was in Germany larshyear and it was *foul*, absolutely *murky*."

(Murky is the current school word.)

"Murky old country France must be if you can't even drink the water there," says Molly.

"It's not. It's super," says Victoria. "Gorgeous cakes. MMM!" She rubs her tummy and rolls her eyes. "And I say, Miss Garth, who jew think I saw at Victoria station on the way home?"

"Me," says Louise, quite spoiling the effect. "I was there with Mummy and we'd come to meet Uncle Howard because he'd come over from Switzerland to marry Mummy and they had a sort of office, un-church wedding and a party afterwards at the um – um – Something-or-other Hotel which was awfully grand and I had five ice-creams and there were millions of people there, except Daddy, of course, but he's coming down to see me at half-term."

"My brother's coming to take me out at half-term," says Penelope. "He's got a new car it's a Bugatti and it absolutely whizzes." She gives a realistic rendering of the noise it makes.

"Swank-pot," says Molly.

I am enjoying myself, being borne along on this

bubbling tide of chatter and learning a good deal about each of the chatterers. The acquisition of such knowledge is far from being a waste of time in my dealings with them and in what I expect them to achieve. Reluctantly I get down to work.

When I have finished with IIB I am due to take Bunty Potts for a private lesson, but she is one of the 'flu victims so I have a free period. I go down to the drawing-room and find Simmy curled up on the sofa, looking through exercise books, with a companionable fire fluttering beside her.

"Hullo," I say, "what have you done with your little lot?"

"Minty has decided to take them out for a Nature Walk, now that the rain has stopped. Suits me, though I shouldn't think it will do her cold any good."

She yawns and settles deeper into the cushions. I kneel on the hearthrug and hold my hands to the warmth.

"This place seems to be wrapped in gloom today," I say, "except for IIB. Nothing takes the bounce out of them. What's wrong with everybody?"

"Well, first there's Robby. I suppose you know about her?"

"Dorothy said something about her being even odder than usual and Penelope Studeley has just told me she's gone potty."

"Oh dear. It's not quite as bad as that. It's just that the hand-washing habit has become worse. She rushes off to scrub up after every lesson now, so the next class is cut short by about five minutes. And, at meals, she washes every plate, knife, fork, spoon and cup she is going to use, even though it's been washed already. And she keeps muttering to herself."

"Is she seeing a doctor or anybody?"

"No, she won't. Tarrant thinks she's too odd to stay on here and Minty thinks she's too pathetic to be sent out into the great, wide world, after all that world has done to her in the past. They've had hell's own rows about it, but Tarrant's quite determined, so the poor old thing is to go at the end of this term. I gather she has no relations apart from Minty, and not a soul in the world who cares tuppence about her. No money either. She lives here during the hols, you know."

Simmy goes on correcting books. I stare into the fire, wondering what horrific experiences have brought Robby to this state and what will become of her.

Presently Simmy says, "I'm leaving too, you know." I didn't know, but having heard about the Indian friend, I am not altogether surprised. It is embarrassing to have been told more about Simmy than she thinks I know and I hope she will tell me about it.

"Oh, *no*, Simmy," I say. "Why? Have you got a better job?"

She smiles faintly and wraps her arms about her.

"I've been given the sack," she says lightly. "Nothing like Robby's trouble, I'm glad to say."

I look at her, heavy and relaxed on the sofa, her round face placid in the pale, winter light. She raises her head and stares into the fire. Her half-closed eyes change in an instant, as a cat's will change, from contentment to wariness. She is no comfortable pussy now; she is implacable Cat.

"When Priscilla and I go to the cottage, we live as we choose, come and go as we please, see who we like. If gossiping neighbours don't approve of my habits, they can do the other thing. Apparently, at least one of them doesn't approve and has told Tarrant so. As I refuse to change my private life and Tarrant evidently thinks it threatens the good name of the school, I'm to go."

This is evidently all I'm to be told. I ask her if she will get another job.

"Oh, yes, I shall have to," she says. "Not necessarily

teaching. I've been a secretary, a waitress, a mother's help, a companion-chauffeuse. Something will turn up. It always does. Priscilla, of course, complicates things a bit. I'm determined to keep her with me and anyway there's nowhere else she can go.''

She swings her legs off the sofa, stands up and stretches hugely, all in one, flowing movement. There is a knock on the door and Priscilla comes in to tell her mother about the Nature Walk. As the child talks, Simmy strokes her dark hair gently, rhythmically.

I go to my next lesson.

Dorothy awaits me in the bathroom, sitting on the edge of the bath, very neat and sleek and glowering. She is seventeen and seething with a variety of talents. She is far and away my best pupil here or at any other school. Now she responds gruffly to my greeting and is then so unusually silent that I have to do what she evidently hopes, and ask what's wrong.

''Nothing,'' she says, dying to be pressed. I oblige. She bursts out.

''I'm just so fed up with school. It's time I left. I'm too old to be here.'' She looks at me sharply to see if I will laugh at her. Remembering the heavy weight of seventeen years, I do not laugh.

''Mrs Minton keeps on and on about 'joining in school life'. Even Miss Tarrant says I haven't any 'community spirit'. Just because I prefer being on my own to listening to the piffling chatter in the common room. One can't be alone here, however hard one tries. Everything has to be done in a herd. I don't really know why but I get so jolly *fed up*,'' she says, working herself up to the brink of tears.

If only I could comfort the girl with words of kindly wisdom, good advice and cheer! At seventeen I felt much the same as she does now. All I can do is to provide a listening ear while she talks on and on. Life for the natural

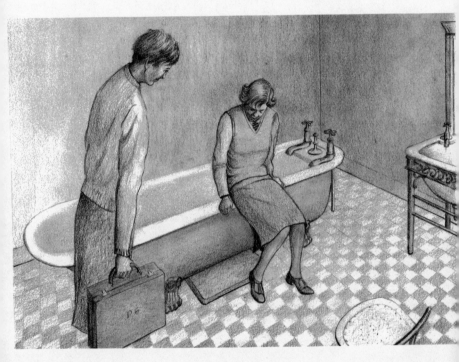

. . . *fed up with school*

loner is not easy at a boarding school, but she has only to stick it out for a few more terms and then, as I tell her, she has a bright future.

After a time I ease her into doing some work and it is, as usual, the work that refreshes and restores her so that, before she goes, she is even able to laugh at herself a little.

ST JOSEPH'S CONVENT - 2

MY little old Austin buzzes and rattles along to the various schools and I'm delighted with her, even though she is far from wind- and weather-proof. It has taken much study of maps and peering at signposts to discover the best routes and I still allow far more time than is necessary for each journey. Even so, I have to concentrate like mad to avoid getting lost. Perhaps, by the end of this term, I shan't have to think so hard and be able simply to enjoy each drive.

Today I am bound for St Joseph's and this is the longest and most complicated route of any of them. Somehow or other I lost precious time by taking a wrong turning, and arrived at the convent only a few minutes before I was due at my first class. I backed up to park near the front door, seized my case, rushed to hang up my coat and walked briskly to Form VI. No time for Sister Philip's lovely coffee.

The girls are in a particularly receptive and responsive mood this morning and we have been reading and discussing a Thornton Wilder play for about twenty minutes when Deirdre O'Shea from Form III comes in, her eyes bright with excitement.

"Excuse me, Miss Garth," she says, "but your car's in the ha-ha."

"*What?*" I am incredulous.

"I suppose it sort of rolled in. Sister Aquinas sent me to tell you. It's kind of tilted up and the front's in the ha-ha. I've just seen it."

She can't repress a grin and I see that all the girls are equally amused. I don't smile. I am appalled.

"Carry on reading," I tell them and go with Deirdre to the scene of the disaster.

Sure enough, the car has slipped her moorings, (I knew that handbrake was a bit weak), rolled across the sloping gravel drive, across the lawn, down the unfenced field, and fetched up, nose foremost, in the ha-ha, her rear wheels still on the near bank.

Sister Philip bustles out from the house, voluble with consternation. She is joined by Sister Mary, properly concerned but barely concealing her amusement. Seeing my poor old car in that undignified posture, I suddenly realise that she has probably been a source of amusement to the entire convent ever since I drove her here. I am forced to laugh, though her present predicament is no laughing matter, for how can the poor thing be rescued? How badly is she damaged? How shall I get home today?

I walk across the field to get a closer look. Luckily the ha-ha is too narrow for the car to have plunged to its depths. Impossible to see the extent of the damage.

By now two or three more nuns have come out to see what has happened and there is much tut-tutting and shaking of heads. There are girls peering from first-floor windows and some (including my abandoned Sixth Form) have crept round the side of the house to see the fun. One of them has the decency to come up to me and say "*Poor* Miss Garth!"

Sister Mary dispatches Ruth, a sensible girl, to the neighbouring farm to ask the farmer, Mr Roberts, to be kind enough to come at once with his strongest horse and yards of stout rope.

Mother comes out and all the children vanish, as birds and small animals do at the approach of a buzzard.

"An unfortunate mishap, Miss Garth," she says, "I hope the car is not too badly damaged," and goes back into the house.

Ruth comes panting back to say Mr Roberts will be round as soon as he has finished his dinner, so we all go indoors and Sister Philip hurries to get my lunch. While serving it, she tells me of all the accidents she has seen, heard about or been involved in, each story ending with, "But everyone safe, thank God," or "Thank God not one of them was killed."

Farmer Roberts arrives with a huge cart-horse called Queenie, and plenty of rope. He is a cheerful, amiable man with an evident respect for the nuns and none for me.

"You really should have left her in reverse gear, Miss," he says.

"I know I should. I thought I had," I reply meekly. "It's so good of you to come to the rescue."

From the deft way he lashes the back axle, and the willing efforts of Queenie, it looks as if they've had to do this kind of thing before. The car is dragged back onto the field, where Mr Roberts manages to bend the mud-guards to free the front wheels and take the broken glass from the headlights. Queenie then, without much difficulty, pulls the car across the field and onto the drive. The rope is removed and, holding my breath, I slip into the driver's seat and press the starter. The little car starts at once.

Mr Roberts refuses payment but seems quite glad when I press five shillings into his hand, and Sister Philip hurries out with two sugar-lumps for Queenie. Sister Mary comes to add her effusive thanks to mine and, when farmer and horse have moved off, I apologise for

. . . the willing efforts of Queenie

all the trouble I've caused and ask if I may start for home at once as, having no lights, I simply must get there before dark. But what about my classes?

"Don't worry," she says, "I'll give the girls something to do. Off with you now and, God willing, we'll see you next week.

So I crawl back to London very carefully. People stare as I pass and a few of them wave and cheer.

George is in the mews and, although he is dressed for duty and therefore very grand and proper as a rule, he bursts out laughing when he sees the state of the car.

I am angry with myself, and ashamed, but so relieved at having got safely home that I have to laugh too.

EVENING CLASSES – 2

WE are now well into the second term of the Braithwaite Settlement classes. The Nigerian girl, the policeman and the cookery demonstrator have vanished. A courteous leave-taking would have been welcome but Mr Crawford tells me that this is seldom granted and should not be expected. I feel I have failed these people, though I don't know how I could have helped them. What each of them needed was private tuition and not a heterogeneous class. I carry on with the remaining students and I'm on good terms with them; we know what to expect of each other.

Mrs Cross the German lady and Miss Isaac the corsetière are generally early and sit waiting for me. Mr Westcott strides in on the dot of seven o'clock and the Misses Read (who keep the sweet shop) follow close behind him. The rest are generally about five minutes late.

This evening I am waylaid by Miss Isaac as soon as I enter the building. She comes up close to me, waving a piece of paper covered with large, unruly writing, and speaks only just above a whisper.

"May I hev a word with you, Miss Garth? Ai'd laik to ask your advaice and it's so difficult to speak freely with *men* in the class. Ai dew so wish it was all ladies. You see, dear, we hev a lecturer comin' to the Corsetry

138

Department next week and Ai shall hev to introduce her to the customers. Ectually, she's showin' a film and talkin' about maternity corsets. Most int*eres*tin'. The film shows the baby at each stage before it's born, so you can see just what sort of support the mother needs. Ai just want to make sure Ai'm sayin' the rait thing and Ai'd be so oblaiged if yew'd look through the little speech Ai've prepared.''

I take the paper from her and she gazes earnestly into my face, breathing heavily, which I find so distracting that I'm unable to take in more than a few words.

''. . . expert on figure care . . . the Little Stranger . . . support with freedom . . . Slimform Corsets for the mother-to-be . . . interesting and instructive . . . hearty welcome . . .''

I make one or two encouraging and, I hope, constructive remarks (*sotto voce*, as students pass us on their way to the various classrooms) and hand the paper back to Miss Isaac.

''Oo, thenk yew ever so much, Miss Garth, dear. Yew've given me such confidence. And Ai'll dew mai best to remember what yew told me last term about mai fainal G's. Ai've bin practisin' them.''

In the classroom I start to hear the homework I set for this week. A few students have done quite a lot. It's always the same ones who do. Others pretend they have worked when they obviously haven't done a thing. The rest make various excuses or admit cheerfully, sulkily, defiantly or apologetically that they haven't had time.

After the first class Mrs Brinkworth and a cup of coffee await me as usual. She looks tired and drawn and more like an elderly horse than ever. Bert is deteriorating rapidly, she says, and it's difficult to keep the home cheerful for Meg, though I bet she succeeds in doing so better than most people would in the circumstances. She and Bert always seem to find something to laugh about and she regales me with a spicy joke or two.

Our conversation this evening is more decorous than usual for we are joined by young Reg and Muriel (from the school Dramatic Society) and by the Misses Read, who daintily sip their coffee and nibble their biscuits. Reg and Muriel's devotion to each other is equalled, if not surpassed, by their devotion to the Theatre and they spend every penny they can save on the cheapest seats for the more serious modern plays. They are appreciative, critical and argumentative about everything they see. Now Reg violently stirs his coffee as though mixing a pudding, and tells me about a highbrow amateur production they went to last week.

"It hasn't exactly got a story but there's a lot of action and the dialogue is you know *significant*."

"Like full of meaning," agrees Muriel.

"Meg was in her school play last summer," says Mrs Brinkworth. "She was Titania. She loved it."

"I expect she was ever so good," says the elder Miss Read, politely. Mrs Brinkworth smiles fondly.

"She was pretty terrible, as a matter of fact. Well, I mean, she weighs over nine stone, for a start, and she's only fourteen and short for her age. But she remembered the words all right, I'll say that. She's a wonderful memory, has Meg. I expect that's why they gave her the part."

Muriel asks me whether I think Macbeth and his wife were in love. The Misses Read look rather uneasy. Luckily, before we can discuss the matter, it's time to start the Public Speaking class. Mrs Brinkworth and I hurry away.

I can understand what Mr Westcott says – or most of it – quite easily now, though I can't decide whether he is really speaking more clearly or whether I have just got used to him.

Mr Chadwick continues to impress and madden everybody (I have warned him off politics but he can't resist ocasional sly digs at our "bourgeois society", Miss

Vandersteen to charm them, Mr Dill to bore them, Mr Trench-Stoddard to embarrass them, Mrs Brinkworth to amuse them. Mrs Wilkins does exactly as she is told, adequately and without originality, and her husband struggles to read the notes he has scribbled on old envelopes, on his way to the class.

IT'S the last week of term – and of the year as far as my courses are concerned for there are no evening classes during the summer. When I get to the Braithwaite, Mr Crawford stops me in the hall and hands me a letter.

'Dear Miss Garth,
    Sorry I shan't be with you this week. Bert died last Thursday night. I was with him but luckily Meg was asleep. She and I are going to stay with my sister for a bit. Thanks for everything.
    With kind regards,
    Yours sincerely,
    B.D. Brinkworth
P.S. We did have a good laugh or two, didn't we!'

I show the letter to Mr Crawford and say, "I don't suppose we shall see Mrs Brinkworth again. She's rather a splendid person and I shall miss her. I'm sure coming here helped her a lot."

"Quite a few sad and worried people come along, you know," he says, "and I do think it helps them a bit."

I have the feeling that that cheerful, tired man knows a good deal about all the students, and probably about the tutors too. (Strange that I've not met any of my fellow tutors). Although I've never spent more than a few minutes with him, coming and going, he strikes me as the kind of man who would make himself available to anyone who needed to talk to him, however busy he was, and who would keep a shrewd but kindly eye on the rest

141

of us. Could it be partly because he's a Quaker and this is a Quaker establishment? I shall never know.

Several people in the Speech Training class hadn't realised that this was to be the last lesson of term. When I remind them, there are one or two gratifying murmurs of regret, some looks of surprise, others of indifference. Some of them may come back next year but I expect most, if they come at all, will take courses in other subjects. What they want is an evening occupation, a smattering of some form of 'culture', a chance to meet people of like interests. Braithwaite provides all this. For some it is an escape, for some an opportunity, a testing-ground which may lead to further study elsewhere, or be easily abandoned after a term or two.

I asked everybody last week to bring something to read aloud, recite or talk about for a few minutes. Reg surprises me by reading an extract from the *Daily Mail* in a very fair imitation of a BBC announcer reading the news. Muriel renders the letter scene from *Macbeth* and gives it her all. Mr Westcott reads Psalm 113 and his consonants pop out like hail-stones hitting a drum. Miss Biggs, our verse-speaker, bids us gather our rosebuds while we may, no matter if they sound more like funereal Floral Tributes. I can't say the speech of either Mrs Cross or Miss Isaac has improved, but at least they know what to aim for. The Misses Read can't or won't attempt to utter.

By the time all those who are willing have had their say and I have made my customary speech of thanks and farewell, it is time for coffee. I couldn't quite bring myself to announce Mr Brinkworth's death; it would have cast too dark a shadow over the proceedings. But I tell Reg, Muriel and the Misses Read when we have coffee together and they ask where Mrs Brinkworth is. In their different ways they are sympathetic without being mawkish or over-dramatic.

The Public Speaking class turns into a Question and

Answer session, during which I repeat much of what has been said throughout the course, quoting from various authorities, for I am well aware of my own lack of knowledge and experience and thankful for the information supplied by the public library.

Much to my surprise, Mr Trench-Stoddard, towards the end of the class, gets to his feet and makes a charming little speech of thanks to me, well phrased and fluent. I think he has gained confidence from hearing the struggles of the other students. When he sits down, everybody claps. I should like to clap too because he did it so well but, as the speech was in my honour, it wouldn't be quite the thing, so I make do with a few appreciative words. There is more clapping, a lot of hand-shaking all round, and then we go our separate ways.

PART III

Summer, 1988

FROM THEN TILL NOW

YES, we went our separate ways. After that last term, I never went back to the Braithwaite Settlement. Through most of the rest of 1939 I kept on with the schools but, instead of teaching Evening Classes, enrolled as a part-time student at the London Theatre Studio. It was a demanding, exhilarating course and I wished I could have devoted all my time to it – as my fellow-students were doing – but I still had to earn my living and so limped along behind the rest as well as I could. Even so, I learnt a great deal in the few months before war was declared and it all came to an end.

The War scattered everybody. I lost touch with all the schools, some of which, I know, were evacuated to distant parts of the country and must eventually have returned to their home bases or else been closed down for good. Only those headmistresses and teachers who were willing and able to adapt themselves to post-war conditions and expectations could have survived. Most of them belonged inescapably to the pre-war era.

As for me, I stayed in London through the war, drove an ambulance, worked in various postal-censorship departments and, by chance, took part in a charity revue put on by a clever young producer who had gathered

together a company of actors and musicians, most of whom were professional performers. Among them was a distinguished bass singer whose performances at the Queen's Hall Proms before the war I had often enjoyed. In the course of this show we got to know each other and, by the end of the war, had married, left London and settled in the West Country.

Then

Everything had changed, was changing, would continue to change: education, language, the aspirations and achievements of the amateur dramatic movement and, of course, myself. I taught, lectured, produced plays and operas, wrote and performed in children's plays and stories for the BBC and, after over twenty years of such activities, became a lecturer at a College of Education.

Six years there, a further twenty years since my retirement, and I now look back fifty years to the young teacher who battled her way so purposefully from school to school in those far-off days. I can hardly believe that she and I are the same person.

Now